476

NEW BIOLOGY
15

NEW BIOLOGY

EDITED BY

M. L. JOHNSON

MICHAEL ABERCROMBIE

G. E. FOGG

15

PENGUIN BOOKS

MELBOURNE · LONDON · BALTIMORE

First published October 1953

*

New Biology appears twice a year,
in April and October. Subscrip-
tions are accepted at 9/- for four
issues, post free. Of the previous
volumes, Numbers 2, 3, 4, 5, 11, 12,
13, and 14 are still available. If
there is any difficulty in obtaining
any of these from a bookseller,
they may be had by writing direct
to the publisher.

*

Made and printed in Great Britain
for Penguin Books Ltd
by The Campfield Press, St Albans

CONTENTS

EDITORIAL

PERHAPS the most discussed problem of human biology at present is the apparently growing disparity between the amount of food produced in the world and the number of people to be fed. Professor A. V. Hill in particular shocked many into awareness of the problem by his address to the British Association in 1952, when he asked how far the saving of life by the progress of medicine was ethically justified if its inevitable outcome was the evil of over-population. What can studies of the population problems of animals contribute to the discussion? One of Professor J. B. S. Haldane's points in our first article is that they suggest caution in prediction: caution about the certainty of disaster or of escape from disaster. Investigation of the control of animal population size has shown that the problems are unexpectedly complicated and subtle. At least we know that growing too big for its food is not one of the disasters that commonly happens to an animal population.

Two other articles in this number lie rather more than usual within the fringe of new thinking which precedes and prepares the advance of well-tested knowledge. Professor C. H. Waddington, stimulated by a recent book, discusses the embryological development of pattern, a central mystery or group of mysteries in modern biology. Biologists often talk about accurate observation, which is taken for granted to be a cornerstone of scientific method. But how is it done? Miss M. L. Johnson takes a look at how one learns to become observant. The theory developed has probably interesting points of contrast and comparison with the 'releasers' and 'innate behaviour patterns' which have been a feature of our recent articles on the behaviour of vertebrates.

We continue our descriptions of the major economic plants of the world, usually known to us solely from some highly abstracted product which we rarely think of as part of a living organism, with an account of the coconut palm by Dr Child. Mr Richard Perry summarizes the sort of information which is emerging from bird-ringing, perhaps the largest co-operative effort in biological science.

The number is completed by a Famous Animal and a Famous Plant. The animal is the dogfish, so familiar as the initiation to vertebrate dissection for the zoological novice, but also, which is Professor J. E. Harris's theme, a very important object of classical and contemporary research. The plant is Chlorella, a unicellular alga, already well known to biologists and perhaps to achieve household fame if an inflated human population has to eat it. The author, Dr G. E. Fogg, has joined the editorial direction of *New Biology*.

M. L. J.

M. A.

G. E. F.

ANIMAL POPULATIONS AND THEIR REGULATION

J. B. S. HALDANE

'Elevated as man is above all other animals by his intellectual faculties, it is not to be supposed that the physical laws to which he is subjected should be essentially different from those which are observed to prevail in other parts of animated nature.'–From 'A summary view of the principle of population.' By the Rev. T. R. Malthus, A.M., F.R.S.

PROFESSOR A. V. HILL'S presidential address to the British Association at Belfast* drew attention to some human population problems. Perhaps a study of animal populations may help us to take a more objective view of the problem of our own species than has sometimes been done.

It is not easy to count living wild animals. Apart from sessile animals such as mussels or barnacles, the easiest to count are, paradoxically, the most mobile of all, namely birds. This is because, by another paradox, birds are completely immobile during one stage of their life cycle, the egg, while mammals at the same stage of their life cycle are carried about by their mothers, and other eggs are harder to find and count than birds' eggs. So while we do not know the total number of gannets alive in 1949, we know the total number of nesting pairs rather accurately (see Perry's article in *New Biology 10*, p. 106). Again, it is impossible to count the moths in a square mile of woodland, and it would be very hard to count the caterpillars. But when the pupae pass the winter in the soil, one can estimate their number rather accurately by digging up a hundred square metres of soil, and counting the pupae in each of them.

*In September 1952. Published in *The Advancement of Science*, vol. 9, No. 34, page 93.

It is not so easy to count small mammals such as field mice. If you trap them with killing traps or remove all those caught in more humane traps, new mice will move into an area before all the old ones are caught. Hacker and Pearson (1952) solved the problem by catching them in traps with food and bedding, punching small holes in their ears, and letting them out again. They then came back to the traps so frequently that Hacker and Pearson even obtained quite good growth curves for individuals. They thus got to know almost the whole population of an area individually, and developed an ingenious method to estimate what fraction they had missed. However, one can get a semi-quantitative idea of changes in mammalian population density from records of human predation, such as the trapping and shooting of foxes and lynxes in Canada.

Another method, the only one which is of much value for insect imagines, is trapping, marking, and release of a small fraction of the animals. Thus on 26 August 1938, Dowdeswell, Fisher, and Ford (see Ford 1945) caught 40 *Polyommatus icarus* (Common Blue butterfly) on the Scilly Island of Tean, marked their wings with spots of lacquer, and let them go. Next day they caught 43, of which 5 were previously marked. Thus a very rough estimate of the total population is $\frac{40}{5} \times 43$, or 344. When this was done for a fortnight, much more accurate estimates both of the total, and of 'birth' rates and death rates, were possible.

The densities, of course, vary immensely with the species considered. Salt and his colleagues found the following densities of soil animals per square metre of English meadow in November, based on an average of 20 cores of soil:

264,000 arthropods, of which

164,000 were mites, 61,300 Collembola (spring-tails).

They state that they missed some of the mites, but there were only 673 Diptera, and 191 Hymenoptera, against 617 Pauropoda, an order which is generally regarded as rare, and of which a number were missed. They were probably all *Pauropus huxleyi*. At the other end of the scale Hubert, in the Albert National Park in the Belgian Congo, found 1 elephant for each 8 square kilometres, 1 wart-hog for each 6, 1 lion for each 4, and no less than

3 hippopotami per square kilometre, along with about 40 ante-
lopes of various species.

Populations and densities change. Sometimes the change is
more or less irreversible. The building of London has extermin-
ated field voles, but increased house mice. But even when the
environment changes little, populations fluctuate. There are two
entirely different pictures. Some species fluctuate very little.
Thus the British herons have been counted in certain areas from
1928 to 1952. Generally they are fairly near to a standard number which is never much exceeded. After a bad winter like 1947

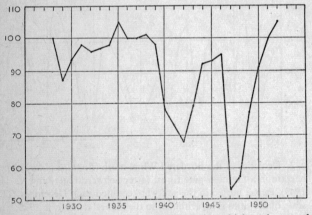

Fig. 1. This graph shows the index number which estimates the
British nesting populations of herons (*Ardea cinerea*). It is based on
nest counts published by Nicholson, and Alexander (1950) from a
number of areas. The figure for 1928 is taken as 100. In the years
1929, 1940, and 1947 the mean temperature of the coldest month
at Norwich was below 0°. In 1934, 1941, 1942, and 1945 it was
between 2° and 0° C. Except for 1934 and 1945, these years, and
especially 1947, caused a big death rate. But the loss was soon made
up, and the density never rose much above 100. The instincts of
herons prevent this. If they, like beavers, could make snow-proof
houses and store food, it would not fall much in hard winters. Will
our species achieve as satisfactory a regulative process as herons
have done?

the population may fall to 60 per cent or so of the standard, but recovers in two or three years (Fig. 1).

Other species fluctuate enormously. Schwerdtfeger's counts of pupae of moth species damaging German pine forests show that the greatest density of the Bordered White (*Bupalus pinarius*) was about 30 per square metre, the lowest density less than one per thousand square metres (Fig. 2). Thus the density could in-

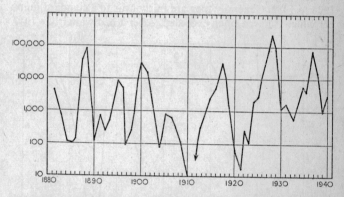

Fig. 2. Densities of the Bordered White moth (*Bupalus pinarius*) per hectare in a German pine forest (after Schwerdtfeger, and Varley 1949). Pupae buried in the soil were counted each December. The scale of densities is logarithmic, so the highest density, in 1928, was at least 30,000 times the lowest, in 1911.

crease over 30,000 times. The Canadian fur-bearing mammals fluctuate in a similar way, but less violently. The annual number of lynxes caught in the Mackenzie area of Canada fluctuates between about 50 and 7,000. We do not, of course, know the population, but if anything the population probably fluctuates less, because lynxes are more likely to be caught when they are numerous and perhaps therefore short of food than when rare. Voles, mice, and lemmings (Elton 1942) fluctuate in the same sort of way.

The fluctuations may be very regular. Lynx maxima occur

about every 10–11 years, vole maxima every 3–4. Or they may be irregular as with the Bordered White.

Clearly a population can only be changed by birth (or hatching), death, or migration. The easiest population to consider is one with strictly defined generations, such as an annual insect. Suppose P_n is the population in an area at a definite date in year n, for example P_{1952} is the number of Bordered White chrysalises in an isolated pine wood on 1 January 1952. Let $P_{n+1} = R_n P_n$, where R_n is the net rate of increase or decrease of the population. R_n can be greater or less than one. But since

$$P_{n+2} = R_{n+1} R_n P_n,$$

and so on, the product of R_n over a number of years must be very close to one, or the sum of the logarithms of R_n very close to zero. How close they must lie is clear if we suppose that $R_n = 1.01$ over 1,000 years, which is a very short time if we are considering evolution. The population would increase 21,000 times. Similarly, if R_n were 0.99 it would decrease to .000043 of its original number.

The problem is not quite so simple when generations overlap. Shall we take our unit time as the average age of mothers of all offspring, or the average of mothers and fathers, which is not quite the same? If we do so our time unit alters with time. Or shall we take R as the ratio of the total population in 1953 to that in 1952, and so on? Every method has its difficulties, and any exact treatment involves at the very least the use of the integral calculus. Nevertheless, an exact theory is possible, and most of the conclusions derived from considering annual generations can be extended to the general case.

Since no population increases without limit, and species only occasionally become extinct, there must be some regulating factors which, on the whole, cause the density of an animal or plant species in a given area to increase when it is small, and to decrease when it is large. Smith called these density-dependent factors. It is perhaps better to call them negative density-dependent factors to distinguish them from factors, also dependent on density, which act in the opposite way, and make for instability. As the density increases, the death rate at any age may increase, the birth rate may fall off, the emigration rate may rise, or any combination of these may occur.

The word 'density' does not necessarily mean density per unit area. For example, the density of some deer species is kept down by infectious disease contracted at contaminated water holes. The number per square mile could be increased by digging out blocked springs. The effective density was thus not the number per square mile, but the number per drinking place.

The relations between P_n and R_n must be something like that

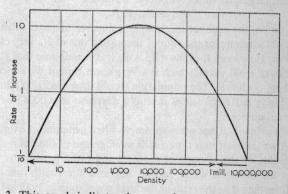

Fig. 3. This graph indicates the sort of way in which the rate of increase of a population per year, or per generation, may vary with the density. The abscissa represents the density of the population, say insects per square kilometre, the ordinate their rate of increase at this density. Both scales are logarithmic. If the density is between ten and a million it increases next year. If it less than ten or over a million it decreases, as shown by the arrows below the figure. There are two possible equilibria, at densities of ten and a million. The lower one is certainly unstable. The upper one is stable if the slope of the graph is gentle enough. With the shape shown there would be slowly damped oscillations round it. The 'optimum' population with the greatest length of life (and perhaps the happiest lives for individuals) would probably have a density between 1,000 and 10,000. In fact this graph is too simple, because negative density-dependent factors such as disease may take several generations to build up.

of Fig. 3. Further, a negative density-dependent factor may be immediate or delayed. That is to say if P_n is large, this may mean that R_n is small, or if the effect is delayed by say 3 years, it may mean that R_{n+3} is small. Clearly a delayed density-dependent factor will favour oscillations. For suppose the population to be in equilibrium when $P_n = p$ over a number of years. If it were suddenly reduced by a disaster, it would show no tendency to increase till three years had elapsed, but would then do so, and go on increasing for three years after it had increased beyond the equilibrium value p.

Before we consider the facts let us make one more theoretical point. Suppose the negative density-dependent factor to be immediate, but weakly dependent. For example, if p is the equilibrium value, suppose that when the population is px, $R = \dfrac{1}{\sqrt{x}}$, then a population of $.5p$ would increase to $.71p$ after one year, to $.84p$ after two years, and so on, never over-shooting the equilibrium; and similarly, if the population were $2p$, it would fall to $1.41p$, $1.19p$, and so on, in successive years. But if we had $R = \dfrac{1}{x^2}$, it would rise from $\frac{1}{2}p$ to $2p$, falling back again, and oscillating indefinitely. If R were $\dfrac{1}{x^3}$, it would rise from $\frac{1}{2}p$ to $4p$, fall to $\frac{1}{16}p$, and so on, the oscillations increasing. In fact, for stability, the regulation, whether immediate or delayed, must not be too sensitive.

We have so far overlooked the fact that in most animal species, including all bisexual ones, and in many plant species, there are positive as well as negative density-dependent factors. When the density falls below a certain value the population decreases still further. One reason for this is the necessity for the sexes to meet. Professor A. V. Hill used to import *Rana ridibunda* from Hungary. In 1935 he gave six pairs to a friend who put them in a Kentish pond. Their descendants have colonized Romney Marshes, and probably number several millions (see Smith 1951). When war broke out in 1939 about fifty were dumped into the Cam, but by next spring they had dispersed so that no male found a female, and the stock died out. Animals whose density is low, such as many moth species, can only survive if the sexes can find one another at great distances. The 'cooperation' may be purely biochemical. Blowfly larvae digest meat by secreting enzymes which act outside them. A single larva does not produce enough to digest the meat around it, and starves to death. Again a single pair may be psychologically unable to mate. Fraser Darling found that a single pair of gulls will not breed. A number of pairs are needed for the necessary psychological stimulation. In social animals mutual aid of a more complicated character is, of course, shown. Finally a very small population may perhaps die out, and is likely to become somewhat weak and sterile, as the result of inbreeding.

Fig. 3 implies that when the population in an area lies between certain limits it will increase; if it lies outside them it will decrease, as shown by the arrows. Thus there are two possible equilibria. The lower one is certainly unstable, the higher one may be stable, or there may be oscillations round it. Lysenko has recently stressed the importance of the ascending part of the curve, where an increased density raises the rate of increase of population. He has wrongly accused 'bourgeois biologists' of neglecting it, when such a book as Allee's (1949) is largely concerned with it. He has also pointed out quite correctly that animals rarely kill members of their own species violently, or even indirectly by starving them. However, Elton and others had anticipated him; and there is always a negative density-dependent factor of some kind, though it usually involves the activity of another species. Professor Hill's speech will, however, doubtless be used to justify Lysenko's equally one-sided standpoint.

Now for negative density-dependent factors. Malthus wrote of 'the constant tendency of all animated life to increase beyond the nourishment prepared for it'. Elton (1930), whose book is still very well worth reading if you can get it, was one of the first to deny this. For example, plenty of birds die of hunger every English winter when the ground is covered with snow for weeks on end. More accurately, perhaps, they die of cold, but would not do so if they had enough food for adequate heat production.

But this is not to say that thrushes starve because the other thrushes have eaten all the available food. Similarly, Varley (1947) showed that in no case were even half the available flower heads parasitized by the gall-forming fly which he studied. If starvation were ever a limiting factor in nature, we should expect it to be so for the Bordered White, whose caterpillars occasionally become so common as to eat most of the needles on pine trees. Now in Fig. 2 an obliquely ascending straight line would represent an increase in geometrical progression (or by compound interest if an economic metaphor is preferred). If the insects increased till they were largely destroyed by famine the graph would look like a saw, with periods of uniform increase followed by a violent drop. In fact decreases occurred in about as many years as increases.

Ulyett (1949) showed that famine can be the limiting factor for blow-flies. He used lumps of 140 gm. of meat. One or a few larvae per lump could not digest it. Of 100 larvae about 80 survived, of 2,000 about 1,000, of 4,000 about 800, producing rather small flies. When 10,000 were put on the meat, none survived, except in the case of the blowfly *Chrysomyia albiceps* which is prepared to be a cannibal, and even of this species only 24 survived. There is good evidence for disastrous famines in Canadian deer, caused mainly by the eating of food by members of their own species. Here, however, the increase was perhaps largely due to the destruction of wolves, which had formerly kept their numbers down. This Malthusian competition is, however, unusual. Such famines are more generally due to the joint activity of a number of species, and the species which mainly causes the famine often escapes. Thus locusts cause famines among men, but largely escape themselves because they are more mobile than men. Crombie (1945, 1946) found that beetle larvae in stored grain kept down their numbers by cannibalism when they become very dense, the older larvae eating the younger.

Competition for space occurs in such animals as mussels and barnacles, but only in very successful sessile species. The commonest negative density-dependent factor is an organism of another species. At first sight we might expect that hawks, owls, foxes, stoats, and other predators would keep down the numbers of small rodents such as field mice. In fact, they cannot be a regulative density-dependent factor for a simple reason, first pointed out by Elton. Supposing the number of field mice in an area to quadruple, the owls may perhaps kill a larger total number than before, but will not check the increase because they cannot increase their numbers as fast as the mice. A predator almost always breeds more slowly than its prey, so if the prey increase greatly over a wide area the predators cannot cope with them, though they may possibly check a local increase by immigration.

On the other hand, bacteria and viruses can multiply far more rapidly than their hosts, and metazoan parasites often a good deal faster. It is doubtful whether parasitic worms play a big part in regulating vertebrate numbers in natural conditions, save in a few species, but parasitic (or parasitoid) insects certainly act as the main negative density-dependent factor controlling some plant-eating insects. They are, however, a delayed factor. Parasites such as *Pteromalus puparum,* which lays its eggs in the pupae of a number of other species, cannot easily act as density-dependent factors on any one of them, for the numbers of parasites depend on the average abundance of many species some months earlier. The most efficient negative density-dependent factor is a parasite species specializing on a particular host species, and adapting its life cycle to that of its host. Thus Varley (1947) studied the gall fly *Urophora jaceana,* which makes galls in the flowers of knapweed, *Centaurea nemoralis,* and its parasites. One of these, *Eurytoma curta,* a chalcid 'wasp', hatches from its pupa a few weeks after its host has laid its eggs, and parasitizes the young larvae. It does not kill them till they have finished their growth, and waits till the next year to emerge. Nicholson and Bailey worked out the mathematics of such a case on the assumption that each female of the parasite species lives long enough to search a certain area for hosts. In Varley's case the area is about 0.5 square yard or about a hundred flower heads. She parasitizes all the host larvae she can find. Hence the fraction of hosts which are killed depends on the density of the parasites. The number of parasites emerging next year depends both on the number of hosts and that of parasites the year before, so control is delayed. For example, when the hosts reach their maximum density the parasites infect say nine-tenths of them, and the number of hosts falls off. But there are then more parasites than hosts, and next year a still larger fraction, perhaps nineteen-twentieths, is affected. So the number of hosts falls violently, that of the parasites following it. Mathematical analysis shows that a complete cycle always takes over four years, and usually less than eight, the maxima and minima for the parasite lagging a quarter of a cycle behind those of the host.

Thus the density of the host species is kept down by the parasites. The density of the parasites is kept down, not by hunger, but by 'egg control'. If they cannot find larvae in which to lay their eggs, they do not lay them.

If there are several parasites, matters are, of course, more complicated, particularly if one is shared with another host. Fig. 2 probably reflects complications of this kind. It must not be thought that immediate and delayed density-dependent factors are mutually exclusive. Lack (1950) showed from Errington's counts of the American bob-white quail *Colinus virginianus* that the mortality between June and November increased with the density, while that between November and April increased with the density two to three years earlier. This could hardly be due to hunger or microbial disease. It could possibly be due to infestation by worms, which builds up much more slowly.

When Nicholson and Bailey (1935) thought about these matters clearly enough to formulate a mathematical theory they had a blinding glimpse of the obvious. That is to say it is obvious now, but had not been so to Darwin, let alone his successors. *The survival of the fittest will only cause the number of animals in an area to increase if the fitness concerns a negative density-dependent factor.* To take a Malthusian example, if the density is limited by the food supply, a gene which makes the animals less conspicuous to a predator or more resistant to cold will be favoured by natural selection, and if it occurs by mutation will spread through the population. But it will not increase the food supply, or the density.

To take a much more realistic case, consider an insect species whose main negative density-dependent factor is attack by an ichneumon fly, but which is also eaten, as a larva, by birds. Let us suppose that a mutation occurs which halves the fraction of larvae killed by birds. More larvae survive to pupate, but more parasitized larvae also survive. On Nicholson and Bailey's assumptions the effect will be to increase the density of parasites, but actually to diminish the number of hosts at all stages of their life cycle. We can now begin to answer a question which plagues every naturalist who believes in the theory of natural selection. Why are species well adapted in some respect no commoner than others which are ill adapted? Consider three related moths, all fairly common in London, *Acronycta psi, aceris* and *megacephala*, the Common Dagger, Sycamore, and Poplar Grey. Their caterpillars are rather similar in the early instars. But in the last instar the first has a caterpillar fairly conspicuous to human eyes at least, with bright red spots and a tubercle. The second has a very hairy caterpillar with orange tufts which are thought to be aposematic (warning). The third looks like bird faeces. I suspect that birds eat more caterpillars of *psi,* but they also eat more of its parasites, so this extra predation need not diminish its numbers, and may increase them.

We can now begin to see a little more concretely what specialization means to an animal species. It means that the species is adapted to life in a particular 'niche', for example, the buds of pine trees or the mud of estuaries. It is rare or absent elsewhere. This is often because it is sensitive to a variety of density independent factors with which other species put up. The most important of these may be competition by other species. The worms living in estuaries can stand sudden changes of osmotic pressure. They cannot stand the competition and predation of other species found in muddy shores which are permanently salt. On the other hand these specialists often occur in large numbers where they occur at all. They can cope adequately with density-dependent factors.

Adaptation to negative factors which are not density-dependent, for example frost or drought, is valuable to a species in increasing its range. Near the edge of its range a species is usually rare, and the negative density-dependent factors due to overcrowding are unimportant. Here any genetically determined adaptation which increases individual fitness may increase the density. Unfortunately, it is very liable to be swamped and disappear as a result of immigration from an overcrowded area. That is, perhaps, as Mayr points out, why characteristic subspecies, and even species, often develop on islands, for example our Hebridean and Orkney voles. Such forms may be well adapted for the neighbouring mainland also, but are swamped by migration if they crop up there.

Few bird species have such violent oscillations as those which we have just been considering. In many cases this is because they have evolved a negative density-dependent factor which does not lead to oscillations. This is the territorial system. Male song birds keep other pairs of their own species out of a territory round their nests by singing, threatening behaviour, and sometimes actual fighting. But much of their feeding is in areas which are the territory of no individual or pair. In some other birds such as herons the feeding territory is also private. In most cases we do not know what happens to the birds which, as a result of this system, cannot find suitable nesting sites. But Mr J. Maynard Smith tells me that round Reading the grebes which cannot find nesting sites by suitable ponds nest on the banks of the Thames, where their eggs are commonly swamped by the wash from steamers. As a result of this system the density never rises above a limit set by the average size of a territory. The exception proves the rule. Some sea birds nest in very dense aggregates, under slum conditions where infection due to overcrowding is inevitable. Doubtless they have developed immunity to many infections. However, Fisher (1952) describes an epidemic of psittacosis, a virus disease, among the fulmars of Faeroe and Iceland. It spread to the human population of the southern Faeroes, infecting over 1 per cent of them, and killing a number. Another strain of ornithosis attacks several species of gulls and terns.

Some British species, such as field voles (*Microtus agrestis*) fluctuate with a period of three or four years. The obvious hypotheses as to the cause of the sudden decline were starvation and epidemic disease. Elton, Ford, Baker, and Gardner in 1931 failed to find the faintest evidence of either in the Long-tailed Field Mouse, *Apodemus sylvaticus*. But the mice certainly died. 'Some obscure biochemical or psychological condition in the mouse population', they wrote, 'caused the animals to die (after being brought in from the wild) with the most unusual regularity and rapidity.' We have not got much further in twenty years. Chitty (1952) described the 'crash 'of a number of Welsh field vole populations in 1938 and 1939, and discussed theories about it. So far from the animals starving, their average weight was greater during the period of greatest abundance than before or after. The decline was not sudden, but spread over about three generations. The first generation was apparently normal, the second was rather short-lived and ceased breeding early, the third had very short lives and was almost completely sterile. Chitty puts this down to the effects of strife during the breeding season in the first, overcrowded generation, and some symptoms found in the Canadian snow-shoe rabbit suggest an exhaustion of the adrenal cortex such as that described by Selye. There can, I think, be no doubt that the final account will have to be on psychological as well as physiological lines. Some species, such as the lemming and several locusts, migrate in response to overcrowding, others die of what Shaw called discouragement. It is notable that locusts are influenced by the degree of crowding to which their mothers have been subjected, as Chitty believes that voles are.

Almost everything remains to be found out. Exactly one study exists which contains figures for the causes of death in a few animal species comparable to those of the Registrar-General for our own, and rather less accurate data on fertility. This is Varley's study of the populations of somewhat over 50,000 knapweed galls, a study which, I hope, has opened a new epoch in ecology. It is a paradox that we know more about the causes controlling mortality and fertility in insects than in birds, in birds than in mammals. But we still have not the faintest idea why some species which do not seem to be particularly specialized in their food or habitat preferences are yet rare. Some such species are dense elsewhere, and fairly mobile. We happen to be near the edge of their range. We shall understand the rarity of others when we know more about their food requirements. But in many cases we cannot yet see how competition for food, disease, territorialism, or any other obvious cause, can be a density-dependent factor. Yet if there is no such factor their numbers ought to increase or decrease.

One interesting possibility is this. Euryphagous predators (i.e. those which will eat a large number of different species), such as insect-eating birds, often have to learn that a given object is edible. This is so for cryptically coloured and/or shaped animals, such as stick-like caterpillars. Once they have eaten one they soon find any others in its neighbourhood. But after some time they probably forget their lesson at least in part. Thus so long as it is sufficiently rare, such a caterpillar may be in little danger from predators unless one literally steps on it. But if it becomes common locally the whole population may be wiped out. This hypothesis will be confirmed or disproved by careful observation of animal behaviour.

We know surprisingly little about causes affecting fertility in our own species. Let me take one example. During the 1939–45 war the birth rate rose violently in England, in Czechoslovakia, and in Eire, though the conditions in these three countries were very different. Twenty years ago statisticians were writing about the Twilight of Parenthood, and predicting catastrophic falls in human populations. Now they are concerned at their increase, except in the socialist countries, where it is believed that food and other production can be increased more than proportionately. I venture to doubt whether any of the current predictions can be accepted without question. But perhaps we might learn something about man by studying other mammals.

FOR FURTHER READING

Every issue of the *Journal of Animal Ecology* usually contains at least one paper on the regulation of animal population, and by going through its back numbers you will probably find one bearing on the group in which you are personally interested. The list here suggested mainly deals with British and West European animals. Equally good work has, of course, been done in North America and the Soviet Union, and a little in the tropics and in Australia and South Africa.

In the following list only some of the references to the *Journal of Animal Ecology* are given:

Alexander, W. B. (1950). *British Birds,* **54,** 123–126 (and later).

Allee, W. C.; Emerson, A. E.; Park, O.; Park, T.; and Schmidt, R. (1949). *Principles of Animal Ecology* (London).

Chitty, D. (1952). *Phil. Trans. Roy. Soc.,* B, **236,** 505–551.

Crombie, A. C. (1945, 1946). *Proc. Roy. Soc.,* B, **132,** 362–395; **133,** 76–109.

Elton, C. (1930). *Animal Ecology and Evolution* (Oxford).

Elton, C. (1942). *Voles, Mice and Lemmings* (Oxford).

Fisher, J. (1952). *The Fulmar* (New Naturalist).

Ford, E. B. (1945). *Butterflies* (New Naturalist).

Hacker, H. P., and Pearson, H. S. (1952). *Biometrika* **39,** 389–413 and earlier.

Nicholson, A. J., and Bailey, V. A. (1935). *Proc. Zool. Soc.,* 551–598.

Smith, M. (1951). *British Amphibians and Reptiles* (New Naturalist).

Ulyett, G. C. (1949). *Phil. Trans. Roy. Soc.,* B, **234,** 77–173.

Varley, G. C. (1947). *Journ. An. Ecol.* **16,** 139–187.

Varley, G. C. (1949). *Journ. An. Ecol.* **18,** 117–122.

THE COCONUT

R. CHILD

Photogravure illustrations between pp. 64 and 65

DISTRIBUTION

'THE slender coco's drooping crown of plumes' is the most familiar feature of tropical shores. (Plates 1–7.) The present-day distribution of the coconut palm (*Cocos nucifera* L.) extends over most of the islands and the coasts of the tropics and even in some parts goes outside the tropic zone (see below). The palm is not

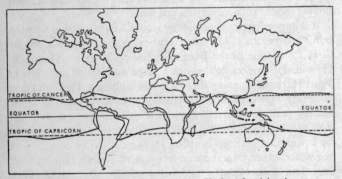

TROPIC OF CANCER

EQUATOR   EQUATOR

TROPIC OF CAPRICORN

Sketch map to show approximate limits of cultivation
of the coconut palm.

necessarily confined to the sea coast or to sea level. There are plantations in Ceylon, in India, and in Indonesia at 2,000-ft elevation. Palms rarely bear much crop when grown at over 3,000 ft, and the farther from the equator, the lower this limit of altitude becomes.

MODE OF DISPERSAL

The world-wide distribution of the palm – even before the era of extensive commercial planting – and its connexion with the sea-shores, led to the idea that ocean currents have been the means of dispersal. In some text-books, indeed, the fruit of the coconut serves as a standard example of the adaptation of a plant to dispersal by sea. O. F. Cook (and other writers) reacted strongly from this view, which he described as a 'time-honoured fallacy'. Readers of *The Kon-Tiki Expedition* will recall that Thor Heyerdahl reported that the coconuts they had in baskets on deck remained eatable and capable of germinating the whole way to Polynesia; but of those they had laid among the special provisions below deck, with the waves washing round them, every one was ruined by the sea water. 'It was', he writes, 'the eyes of the coconuts which sucked in the water and grew soft so that the sea water got through. Or else it was the refuse collectors all over the oceans who took care that no edible thing that floated should get across from one world to another.'

It is impossible to reconcile the Kon-Tiki observation with the published results (1941) of careful experiments carried out by C. H. Edmonson of the Bernice P. Bishop Museum, Honolulu, Hawaii. Edmonson floated out a large number of coconuts in Pearl Harbour, keeping them in place with nets. He found that coconuts were capable of developing after having floated in the sea for periods up to 110 days. A conservative estimate of the distance that might be traversed in that time by a coconut carried by favourable currents is about 3,000 miles. After contact with sea water, experimental coconuts required periods ranging from less than three months to over one year to exhibit visible development. Even granted that, within limits, ocean dispersal can occur, the second question arises – if seed-nuts still viable are cast up by chance on a tropical shore, what are the possibilities of their development and growth? Reference is here usually made to the vegetation of coral atolls, of which coconut palms are a common feature. As Darwin pointed out, atolls must at one time have existed as mere water-washed reefs and 'all their territorial productions must have been transported by the waves of the sea'. However, the occurrence of coconut palms on such atolls may merely mean that these islands were formerly inhabited and for some reason were later abandoned.

More definite is the evidence of volcanic islands. Coconuts were stated to have been among the plants growing on the Krakatoa group when these became restocked after the cataclysm of 1883. In the same area (after more than forty years of quiescence) heavy eruptions from a submerged volcanic crater threw up several new islands in 1928–30; one of these, Anak Krakatoa IV, persisted and eighteen months later was visited by Dr Docters van Leeuwen, who found that many plant seeds had already been washed ashore and had germinated. The strand flora was a typical Barringtonia* association and included 41 germinating coconuts. 'There could be no question at all', wrote Dr van Leeuwen, 'whether the nuts had been planted or not. No native, with the exception of the coolies of the volcanological service, had dared to land on this still active and treacherous crater . . . moreover, the coconuts lay on the beach and were mostly unburied, lying . . . in the same disorderly manner as the seedlings of the other plants, as to which no one questions their distribution by the sea.' Nature, unfortunately, terminated this large-scale experiment by a further volcanic eruption in November 1932.

Of palms having actually established themselves as fully grown trees it is difficult to find well-authenticated examples. A good case has been made out for areas of palms in Trinidad having been self-sown. 'The coconut groves', says H. C. Sampson, 'on the east coast of Trinidad in the region of the Cocal are undoubtedly self-sown. These are said to have originated from the wreck of a French schooner laden with coconuts. One sees the trees growing in clumps often four or five together or in close proximity, which would not be the case had they been planted by man.'

Probably, then, the coconut can unaided traverse long distances and establish itself on open coasts. But such establish-

---

*A plant community, characteristic of tropical sea shores, described by Schimper (*Die Indo-malayische Strand-flora*, 1891), and usually including, as in the present example, *Barringtonia racemosa*, *Pandanus spp.* ('screw-pine'), *Terminalia catappa* ('Indian almond'), etc.

ment must be rare; the young seedling cannot survive in the open
glare of an exposed beach, or when it has to dispute the soil with
other plants. Animal enemies such as wild pigs and fruit-eating
rodents are other factors against its survival. By far the most
active agent in spreading the coconut palm must have been man.
Inland every tree owes its existence to man; on the coast most
of them.

ORIGIN

In view of its present wide dispersal, the task of assigning an
original habitat to the coconut palm is a formidable one. The
question has been much discussed and evidence has been ad-
duced from many different sources – botanical, historical,
archaeological, ethnological. A survey of the evidence therefore
covers a wide and interesting field.

About a hundred years ago a demand began to arise in manu-
facturing countries for coconut oil to be used in soap making. At
the turn of the twentieth century coconut oil came into increasing use as a constituent of vegetable margarine and other edible
fats, and this, like the earlier demand, led to large extensions of
coconut planting. The intense concentration of cultivation in
particular regions is therefore no indication that the palm originated in any of these.

The occurrence of a greater number of varieties and species
is generally taken as evidence of nearness to the origin of the
prototype plant.

Von Martius the systematist (*Historia naturalis palmarum,*
1823–50), placed the probable origin on the West coast of Central America, his principal argument being that all other species
then classified as *Cocos,* as well as related genera of palms, were
found in America. This botanical argument – and it was a strong
one – was modified by the discovery of two new forms of palms
of the Tribe Cocoeae in South Africa and in Madagascar.
Actually the number of varieties (as distinct from species) of the
coconut palm has not been determined with any accuracy, partly
because of the difficulties involved with a plant of such wide
distribution and partly because of lack of genetical purity due

to the fact that cross-fertilization is normal. It now seems clear, however, that there exists in the islands of Polynesia and the Malayan Archipelago, and in Ceylon and India, a much larger number of varieties than in America or Africa.

The most energetic advocate of an American origin has been O. F. Cook (1910). Besides the original botanical argument, he has put forward as worthy of consideration by students of ethnology the 'possibility ... that the primitive agricultural peoples who distributed the coconut and other American plants over the islands and shores of the Pacific and Indian Oceans came originally from America'. This was later the thesis of Thor Heyerdahl of *Kon-Tiki* fame. Cook claimed also that the historical records showed the presence of the coconut in Cuba, Puerto Rico, Brazil, and Colombia at dates so early as to preclude the idea of introduction by Spaniards.

On the other hand, the historical evidence, such as it is, seems strongly in favour of the view that the dispersal of the palm about the Atlantic coasts was due to European nations and occurred after the time of Columbus. The case for a pre-Columbus introduction to the Pacific coast of Panama is more open; but the limited extent of its range there seems to indicate a date not long before 1492. There would be general agreement that the palm is a comparatively recent introduction to West Africa. The palm was in East Africa much earlier, and was found by Vasco da Gama in 1497–98 on the island of S. Jorge, near Beira; nevertheless an early introduction by Arab voyagers is probable; though it has been suggested that its arrival may have been due to sea-drift, like that of *Casuarina equisetifolia* L. and *Barringtonia speciosa* Blume, two eastern strand plants.

As far as Asia is concerned, so long established is the palm in India that early travellers, for example Marco Polo in the thirteenth century, called it *Nux indica,* the Indian nut. There is adequate evidence of its occurrence in India 3,000 years ago. Even so, Indian scholars do not regard it as indigenous; other Indian languages have derived their names for the coconut from the Tamil, which seems to point to an introduction from the south-east. In Ceylon early references to the coconut are scanty;

there is mention in the ancient chronicle, the *Mahavamsa*, of the planting of coconuts by Agrabodhi II about A.D. 589. This monarch is identified with the Kusta Raja whose statue, carved out of the solid rock, is to be seen near Weligama, in the south of the island. He is supposed to have been the first to introduce coconut cultivation into Ceylon, and his legend is related with much romantic embroidery by B. Seemann in his *Popular History of the Palms* (1856). Probably the palms had been growing in South Ceylon for some centuries before his time, but the persistence of the legend may be taken to indicate a time when it had been unknown in Ceylon. Similar considerations apply to the Malay Peninsula, Siam, and Indo-China on the Asiatic mainland.

It seems clear that, whatever the region of origin, the present distribution of the coconut palm – and indeed that of a century ago – has been largely the result of several phases of dispersal by man.

Efforts have therefore been made to define more closely the original habitat of the palm by ethnological considerations. Werth (1932), for example, came to the opposite conclusion from that of O. F. Cook from study of the Malayo-Polynesian culture in which the coconut was an important factor; thus he plotted the range over which was found the coconut scraper, an object of importance as a fat-provider in domestic economy, and found it to coincide roughly with the range over which the outrigger boat was used. Much stress has been laid, too, on the significance of the multiplicity of names for the coconut in the Old World tropics; the centre of the greatest development of specific and varietal names has been the Indo-Malayan region.

Some Eastern limits may perhaps be put on the search for the original home of *C. nucifera* by the modern view of ethnologists that the Polynesian region was populated at a relatively late period. If this view is correct, then a pre-Columbus but not too early chance may have carried the coconut to the Pacific coast of Panama.

We are still left with a reasonably large area in which to seek the original home in the island belt running from 90° E. through the Sunda Islands, Borneo, Celebes, the Philippines, the Moluccas, New Guinea, to the Polynesian Islands. It must be admitted that we cannot and are unlikely to be able to assign to *C. nucifera* as precise an original habitat as that possessed by the so-called 'double coconut' *Lodoicea seychellarum* Labill, in a single island of the Seychelles.

SOME BIOLOGICAL ASSOCIATIONS OF THE COCONUT PALM

There are certain animal species (besides man) closely associated with the coconut palm, and if these are specific to the coconut, or to its near relatives, the association may be regarded as of long standing. When the coconut spread from its place of origin it may or may not have been accompanied by its associates, and so from a study of their range we may get clues as to the place of origin of the coconut.

(a) *The Crab* Birgus latro *Hbst*

We can hardly better the description of the Robber Crab given by Charles Darwin, who observed it on the Cocos-Keeling Islands in 1836.

I have before alluded to a crab which lives on the coconut: it is very common on all parts of the dry land, and grows to a monstrous size: it is closely allied or identical with the *Birgos latro*. The front pair of legs terminate in very strong and heavy pincers, and the last pair are fitted with others weaker and much narrower. It would at first be thought quite impossible for a crab to open a strong coconut covered with the husk; but Mr Liesk assures me that he has repeatedly seen this effected. The crab begins by tearing the husk, fibre by fibre, and always from that end under which the three eye-holes are situated; when this is completed, the crab commences hammering with its heavy claws on one of the eye-holes until an opening is made. Then turning around its body, by the aid of of its posterior and narrow pair of pincers, it extracts the white albuminous substance. I think this is as curious a case of instinct as ever I heard of, and likewise of adaptation in structure between two objects apparently so remote from each other in the scheme of nature as a crab and a cocoa-nut tree. . . . These crabs are very good to eat: moreover, under the tail of the larger ones there is a great mass of fat, which when melted sometimes yields as much as a quart bottle full of limpid oil.

An analysis of this fat by Hilditch and Murti at Liverpool in 1939 showed it to resemble coconut oil and to have very little of the character of a marine animal fat.

It seems inadmissible that such an organism as *B. latro* could have been specifically evolved independently of the coconut; and certain that the original home of the coconut must lie within the range of occurrence of the crab. This does not help a great deal, since the distribution of *B. latro* extends from the Cocos-Keeling Islands as far as the Purdy Islands in the Bismarck Archipelago, and from the New Hebrides to the Palmyra Islands in the Pacific. However, it is unknown on American and African coasts, neither does it occur in India and Ceylon, so that any evidential value that the association of the crab and the coconut may have confirms the provisional conclusions drawn from botanical and historical considerations.

(b) Insects

For an important economic crop, widely and extensively grown, the coconut has perhaps not received from research workers its fair amount of attention. Nevertheless much *ad hoc* research work has been carried out in coconut-growing countries, and is to be found scattered widely through a diversity of journals. Certainly the palm has not lacked the attention of entomologists. Further evidence of the place of origin of the plant may be obtained from the number of insect species which are specific to it; where the number is greatest is likely to be the place of origin. P. Lepesme, in his encyclopaedic work *Les Insectes des Palmiers* (1947), lists the palms in the order of the number of insect species reported in association with them. *C. nucifera* heads the list with 751, of which 165 or 22 per cent are specific to the genus. In the Melanesian area are found 81 species of which 74 or 90 per cent are specific on *Cocos*. In Africa are found 111 species of which 4 only or 3.6 per cent are specific to *Cocos*, though they may infest palms generally. In

America *Cocos* harbours 217 species of which 44 or 20 per cent are specific to *Cocos*. Such figures, concludes Lepesme, are very significant and all in favour of a Melanesian origin for *C. nucifera*. The Melanesian area is generally regarded as extending from the Equator southward to the Tropic of Capricorn between 145° and 180° E., i.e. roughly from New Guinea to Fiji. The weight of the evidence is in favour of an original home for the coconut somewhere in this region; any attempt further to localize it is probably fruitless in the present state of knowledge.

WORLD ACREAGES

It is only possible to obtain an approximate idea of the total acreage of coconut palms in the world. In most countries where they grow the larger proportion of the palms are in the village holdings for which statistics are non-existent. Before the war Leo Schnurmacher, Inc., of Manila, made an ambitious effort to estimate world acreages and production, as did also the International Institute of Agriculture, Rome, and the old Empire Marketing Board in the U.K.

In round figures the total world area of coconut palms is put at not less than 10 million acres carrying some 500 million palms. The annual production in terms of coconut oil is estimated at 3 million tons, or sufficient to supply a fat ration of 40 lb. per head per annum for 7 per cent of the world's population. Of this total production roughly a half is consumed, mostly domestically, in the countries of origin; the other half – the exportable surpluses – enters world commerce.

Ninety per cent of the world's exportable coconut products comes from five large producing areas: Indonesia, Philippines, Ceylon, Malaya, and Oceania. India, a large producer, consumes all its own production, and is now in fact a considerable net importer. Why has commercial coconut growing developed particularly in these areas? Climatic and edaphic conditions are favourable, but so they are elsewhere. Another factor seems important, namely accessibility. Indonesia, the Philippines and Oceania are made up of hundreds of large and small islands;

Ceylon is an island, Malaya is a peninsula. In archipelagos, islands, and peninsulas the length of the coastline is very considerable, its ratio to the area of the country reaching very high figures. Thus to favourable climate and soil conditions must be added an economic factor, that of transport facilities.

The question arises why the West Indian archipelago is not such a prominent coconut-producing area. It would seem that the ethnographical element must be considered. The great centres have been largely those influenced by the seafaring peoples of Malayo-Polynesian origin.

INSECT PESTS AND THEIR CONTROL

Of the 751 species of insects listed by Lepesme as infesting the coconut palm, fortunately only a few are serious pests.

There are two genera of *Coleoptera* which together cause enormous damage to various cultivated palms, especially *C. nucifera* and *Elaeis guineensis,* namely *Oryctes* and *Rhynchophorus*. Over twenty species of *Oryctes* have been distinguished on morphological grounds, but their habits are much the same; the *O. rhinoceros* L. which occurs widely from Ceylon and India to New Guinea and Samoa, may be taken as typical. Unlike most other Coleoptera it is the adult beetle which is responsible for most of the damage; it is one of the largest of the Lamellicornia, attaining a length of 5 cm. On the head is a recurved horn – hence the specific name. The adult beetle can bore into the crown of palms, causing damage to the terminal bud and leaving the way open for even more serious injury by *Rhynchophorus* species. Of the several species, *R. ferrugineus* Ol. inhabits the Indo-Malayan and Melanesian regions. In contrast to *Oryctes,* this only causes damage in the larval state. Attack by *Rhynchophorus* ('red weevil') usually follows damage by *Oryctes* or mechanical injury; the female lays its eggs in the injured tissues; the larvae which hatch out tunnel and feed inside the stem and eventually the palm is killed.

Ordinary plant sanitation measures are adequate to control these two pests. *Oryctes* breeds in decaying vegetable matter, dead and decaying logs, manure heaps and the like. The crowns of dead palms often harbour large numbers and in most coconut-growing countries it is made compulsory by law to fell and burn dead trees. The larvae of *Oryctes* are parasitized by the Green Muscardine fungus *Metarrhizium anisopliae* Metch. (an Hyphomycete similar to that which caused the silkworm disease investigated by Pasteur in 1865), but attempts to control the pest by means of the fungus have not been successful. This is in line with most attempts to use entomogenous fungi to induce epidemics, for example amongst scale insects and white fly (*Trialeurodes vaporariorum,* Westw., a greenhouse pest).

Recently in India it has been shown that Gammexane is very lethal to *Oryctes* larvae and effective control was obtained by its application to potential breeding places.

The Scale Insect *Aspidiotus destructor* is a pantropical species which is found wherever the coconut palm occurs; it was first described by Signoret in 1869 on material from Réunion. Other palms are attacked and also such plants as the banana, guava, paw-paw, and sugar cane. Infected fronds are covered on the upper surface with yellow patches made up of countless yellow spots, each of which marks the position of a scale on the under surface. The insects suck the sap from the soft leaf tissue and the leaves finally wither and die. In India and Ceylon the damage caused by *Aspidiotus* is seldom serious, since it is controlled by its natural enemies, notably the small blue-black Coccinellid (ladybird) beetle *Chilocorus nigritus* F. In some island areas the scale had become introduced without its natural enemies, with in consequence a marked multiplication of the pest and considerable damage to palms; in these areas biological control has proved very effective.

It is generally agreed that successful biological control of insect pests has mainly been achieved in island groups; there is no instance of success over larger areas. The ravages of *A. destructor* in Mauritius were markedly reduced by the introduction of *Chilocorus politus* Muls. and *C. nigritus*. Even more striking was the campaign against *Aspidiotus* in Fiji. The Coccinellid *Cryptognatha nodiceps* Mshl. was introduced from Trinidad and the incidence of *Aspidiotus* was reduced to negligible proportions.*

Fiji has been the scene of other classical examples. The larval stage of the moth *Levuana iridescens* Baker feeds on the leaves of the coconut palm, eating away all but the epidermis and cuticle. Formerly confined to Vita Levu, the moth by 1925 had spread to Ovalau and the neighbouring islands and constituted a real threat to the coconut industry, an outstanding factor in the economy of Fiji. In a little more than a year the pest was completely suppressed by the introduction of a Tachinid parasite *Bessa* (*Ptychomyia*) *remota* Ald. from Malaya. Another example of successful biological control in Fiji was that of the Leaf-mining Beetle *Promecotheca reichei* Baly. This was of particular interest since *Promecotheca* is indigenous to Fiji. There was, says Taylor in his account of the campaign, 'a vague, but prevalent belief that an insect is much more difficult to control biologically in its native environment than elsewhere. For this belief, however, there is no justification, except in a few special instances.' *Promecotheca* had its own indigenous parasites in Fiji, but its equilibrium with these was upset by the arrival of the mite *Pedicaloides ventricosus* Newp. The mite periodically eliminated all the development stages, except one, of the beetle, thus producing a condition similar to that of insects in temperate climates, where development and time of occurrence are controlled by seasonal climatic changes, and successive generations cannot overlap. 'The native parasites proved ill adapted for coping with this new condition, being unable, so long as it prevailed, to multiply continuously. *P. reichei* anomalously became a pest in the presence of the very parasites that normally controlled it.' Search was then made for the special type of parasite required to overcome the obstacles which the indigenous parasites could not overcome; of four possible from Java, *Pleurotropis parvulus* Ferr. was chosen for introduction to Fiji; it is an internal parasite of the larva and pupa of a coconut leaf-miner

*A popular account of the campaign against *A. destructor* in Fiji is given by H. Nicol in *The Biological Control of Insects* (Pelican Book, 1943), pp. 73 *et seq.*

(*Promecotheca nuciferae* Maulik), of Java and Celebes. In Fiji it attacked *P. reichei* as readily as it did its normal hosts in Java.

Of the 751 insects reported on the coconut palm, 323 are Coleoptera (beetles), 165 Hemiptera (bugs) and 115 Lepidoptera (moths and butterflies). A number of the latter – mostly their caterpillars – are more or less serious pests of the palm. One more example may be given from India and Ceylon, the Black-headed Caterpillar *Nephantis serinopa* Meyr., which unchecked is capable of defoliating palms completely. It came into prominence about 1919 in the Eastern Province of Ceylon and along the Malabar coast of India, and much study was devoted to its natural parasites. In the wet zone of Ceylon natural control is due to the Eulopid parasite *Trichospilus pupivora* Ferr.; the latter will not establish itself in the drier regions of East Ceylon, but a measure of control has been achieved by the liberation at suitable times of large numbers of parasites bred at a laboratory of the Department of Agriculture.

PREMATURE NUTFALL

Like the Tree of Life of Revelation xxii. 2, the coconut palm 'beareth her fruit every month'. At approximately monthly intervals new flowering branches are produced; the female flowers, relatively few in number, appear at the base of the panicle; above them are the numerous male flowers. From the emergence of the spadix to complete maturity of the fruit takes twelve to thirteen months; at any one time, therefore, a palm is carrying twelve or more bunches at successive stages of development. (See Plates 4 to 6.)

The fall of immature nuts (the so-called 'button nuts') within two months of the emergence of the spadix is a normal phenomenon, since far more female flowers are produced than the palm can bring to maturity – under average conditions in Ceylon, about 29 to 35 per cent produce ripe fruit.

The fall of immature nuts at a later stage often causes considerable losses of potential crop; it occurs particularly when the fruits are almost fully grown, but before the endosperm or 'meat' has begun to form. It may be due to drought, fungus disease, insect attack, and other adverse factors. A particularly interesting example occurred in the British Solomon Islands Protectorate; here immature nutfall was so severe on many plantations that little crop was left on the palms. By 1938 the trouble had been traced to the activities of a sucking bug – *Amblypelta cocophaga* China. This insect pierces and sucks the plant with its needle-like mouth parts, the usual point of attack being the female flowers and young nuts in the softest parts near the stalk; this leads to the premature fall of the fruit. A very small population of these bugs can completely destroy the crop from a palm as they feed on the successive bunches of flowers. A check on the pest's activities is provided by the large red ant *Oecophylla smaragdina* F. It was observed that palms carrying the nests of these ants carried also good crops; the ants, in fact, seized or drove away the bugs. The equilibrium was upset by invasions of other species of ants, notably *Pheidole* species, which drove off the red ants but did nothing themselves to check the bugs. After the 1939–45 war it was found that the ecological balance had been somewhat restored in favour of the red ants and ripe coconuts. Observations suggested that this was due to the increase of undergrowth and fallen debris occasioned by neglect during the war. *Pheidole* ants nest at the base of palms and the red ants, whose nests are up the trees, can only pass freely to the ground, and thence to other trees, if a bridge of creepers or fallen fronds by-passes their enemies' strongholds.

A very similar state of affairs has recently been found to exist in Zanzibar and the coastal districts of Kenya and Tanganyika. In these areas it had been known for many years that a limiting factor in coconut production was premature nut fall, accompanied by 'gummosis' – the production of distorted undersized fruit exuding a hard gummy substance. These diseases had been ascribed to various causes; thus the Kenya Department of Agriculture Report for 1931 says, 'Malformations of nuts, such as occur in gumming, and the shedding of young nuts, were found to be physiological diseases, gumming probably being due to soil deficiencies, and shedding associated with particular conditions of soil moisture.' The true solution came to light in a most unexpected way as a by-product of research on a quite different problem.

Most of the world's supply of cloves comes from the islands of Zanzibar and Pemba, situated off the East Coast of Africa just south of the equator. During the present century losses of clove trees have been increasingly serious from what became known as 'Sudden-death disease', and in 1947 a special research team was organized to investigate. It was soon settled that the observed phenomena could only be explained by the presence of a pathogen, and at one stage of the investigation the possibility of its being a virus was explored. Careful search was made for possible insect vectors and the only one which seemed a likely culprit was a scale, a *Saissetia* species, which is tended and transported by the African red tree-ant *Oecophylla longinoda* Latr. In the course of study of the habits of this ant, it was found to be a predator on other insects, including a bug, a *Theraptus* species. Very soon *Theraptus* was shown to be responsible for the nutfall and 'gummosis' so long observed in East Africa and the island of Zanzibar. Like *Amblypelta,* this bug makes punctures through the calyces of the female flowers and into young fruits, on which necrotic areas develop. Flowers damaged in the bud stage are destroyed, but if the attack occurs after pollination the nuts may develop to maturity but show marked deformity. When palms are colonized by the ant *O. longinoda,* Theraptus attack is minimized and good crops develop. In many areas, however, *O. longinoda* is driven off by such ground-nesting ants an *Anoplolepis longipes* Jerd., *A. custodiens,* and *Pheidole* spp., and crops of coconuts are practically nil.

As the coconut industry is of economic importance to Zanzibar second only to cloves, entomological research was immediately switched over from cloves to coconuts, two clear lines of study being (i) the ecology of various ant species with the object of finding conditions most favourable to *O. longinoda,* and (ii) the possibility of insecticidal control of the bug *Theraptus.* Spraying or dusting with Gammexane preparations was effective for the latter purpose, but tended to favour the spread of *Aspidiotus destructor,* the Coconut Scale, by killing off the controlling ladybirds; more complete success has been obtained with a DDT preparation. This piece of work, originating in a different problem, bids fair to add some millions of coconuts to E. African production, and provides a cogent argument against too rigid planning of research.

ECONOMIC PRODUCTS OF THE COCONUT PALM

The local uses of the coconut are innumerable. Dwellings are thatched with coconut fronds; the water of the unripe coconut provides the most wholesome fresh drink in the tropics. The inflorescences are tapped for toddy, a sugary liquid which rapidly ferments to give a mildly alcoholic beverage. Distillation of the latter yields arrack, a spirituous liquor akin to rum.

The principal primary product of economic importance is *copra*, the dried endosperm or meat of the nut. This is exported as such, though there is an increasing tendency for it to be crushed for oil in the countries of origin. A ton of copra yields approximately 12 cwt. of coconut oil and $7\frac{1}{2}$ cwt. of coconut cake. The latter is well known as a cattle food, containing about 20 per cent of protein. Corresponding then to the annual world output of 3 million tons of edible oil, there is also an output of 375,000 tons of protein.

Of commercial importance in Ceylon and the Philippines is desiccated coconut. In the manufacture of this commodity, the brown skin of the kernel is pared off, leaving only the white meat; this is washed in running water, and passed through a shredder. Finally, the shredded or grated nut is dried in hot-air dryers similar to those used for tea. Desiccated coconut is used in the manufacture of biscuits, confectionery and the like, and also domestically in cakes, sweets and puddings; it is the only coconut product which reaches the retail consumer direct.

A range of by-products comes from the husk, from which the fibre is extracted by hand (on a cottage industry scale) or by machinery. In either case there are obtained the long bristle fibres, often 12 inches or more long, and a larger quantity of shorter fibres known as mattress fibre. The former is used for making brooms and the like, and the latter for stuffing mattresses, car cushions, and upholstery. Coconut fibre or coir is spun into rope, which is very hard and durable, resists the action of salt water, and has been used on ships from time immemorial. Coir mats are another familiar manufactured product.

Coconut shells afford a hard charcoal, which is a good basis for gas-adsorbent charcoals; it was much used in the manufacture of gas masks and during the four years 1937–40 Ceylon exported some 60,000 tons of crude coconut charcoal valued at about £300,000.

Some idea of the relative importance of these various commercial products may be obtained from the amount and value of coconut products exported from Ceylon in 1950. The Ceylon acreage is estimated at rather more than a million, which exceeds that of tea and rubber together.

Coconut Products Exported from Ceylon in 1950

		£
*Fresh Coconuts	8,631,794 nuts	303,795
Coconut Oil	75,717 tons	9,553,061
Copra	21,117 tons	1,907,675
Desiccated Coconut	44,909 tons	7,142,847
Coconut Cake	8,942 tons	189,919
Mattress Fibre	43,692 tons	1,192,369
Bristle Fibre	8,928 tons	371,208
Coir Yarn and Ropes	4,525 tons	345,286
Coir Manufactures (and Mats)	327 tons	23,002
Coconut Shell Charcoal	4,062 tons	46,301

£21,075,463

The products derived from the kernel of the nut – viz. copra, coconut oil and desiccated coconut – account for over 90 per cent of the value. However, the husks and shells are not utilized to the full.

The importance of the coconut palm both in the external and internal economy of producing countries has been increasingly realized, and research on agricultural and technological im-

*A wet Bank Holiday in England has a noticeable effect on the number of coconuts imported!

provement is being actively pursued in India, Ceylon, Indonesia, the Philippines and elsewhere. To produce a ton of coconut oil, about 8,000 coconuts are required. The average world production per acre per annum is probably somewhere in the neighbourhood of 2,000 coconuts or about 5–6 cwt. of oil. An ordinary well-cared-for estate in Ceylon can yield at least double this quantity, and crops equivalent to 15 cwt. of oil per acre are not unknown. By the application in all coconut-growing countries of existing technical information, and extended research on local problems, the world's fat supplies could be increased by several hundred thousand tons annually at a fraction of the cost of clearing land for the same production from annual crops. As Sir John Russell said in his Presidential Address to the British Association in 1949: 'Most countries could increase their food production considerably by applying known methods of improvement and raising the average performance to the level of the best', and 'Pure science is continuously opening up new possibilities for use in agriculture.'

REFERENCES

Child, R. 'Recent Research on the Coconut Palm with Special Reference to Ceylon.' *Empire J. of Exper. Agric.*, **18**, 177–89 (1950).

Edmonson, C. H. 'Viability of Coconut Seed after floating in Sea.' Occasional Papers of Bernice P. Museum, Honolulu, Hawaii, Vol. XVI, No. 12, 293–304 (1941).

Heyerdahl, Thor. 'American Indians in the Pacific.' Part VII. 'Botanical Evidence of Polynesian Routes: The Coconut.' pp. 453–65. (London: Allen and Unwin) (1952).

Taylor, T. H. C. 'The Biological Control of an Insect in Fiji.' (Imperial Institute of Entomology) (1937).

van Leeuwen, W. Docters. 'Germinating Coconuts on a New Volcanic Island, Krakatoa.' *Nature,* **132**, 674–5 (1933).

Way, M. J. 'An Insect Pest of Coconuts and its Relationship to Certain Ant Species.' *Nature,* **168**, 302 (1951).

Werth, E. 'Verbreitung, Urheimat und Kultur der Kokospalme.' *Ber. Deutsch. Bot. Ges.*, **51**, 301–14 (1933).

SOME RESULTS OF
BIRD RINGING

RICHARD PERRY

To the field naturalist one of the most interesting aspects of modern ornithological research has been the extraordinary extension, during the past fifty years, of marking individual wild birds with numbered leg-rings, either as nestlings or as adult birds caught in special traps or decoys, or sometimes by means of nets. In some instances alternative marking devices are employed: wing-clips on ducks and geese, for example, when too young to band on the leg, as the size of ring used is governed by the thickness of the adult's leg. In some species – the peewit is one – there is little difference in size between the legs of young and adults, and the nestlings can safely be ringed within 12 hours of hatching, without risk of the ring coming off.

Although history records a few isolated instances of the marking of wild birds – such as the white-fronted goose ringed with a collar in Holland in 1800 and recovered 35 years later near Danzig – the pioneer of modern ringing was a Dane, H. C. Mortensen, who marked his first birds with leg-rings in 1899. Five years later ringing began in Britain with starlings, and by 1911 10,000 British birds were being ringed in one season. Today ringing schemes are in operation in almost every European country, from Italy to Iceland and the U.S.S.R.; in India, Japan and South Africa; and on the other side of the Atlantic (including Greenland). In North America the enormous total of nearly half a million birds is ringed annually, compared with a maximum of 85,000 in Britain and a further 100,000 or more over the rest of Europe. In each of these countries there is a central bureau, and/or a number of research stations, where records are filed of all rings issued. Subsequent recoveries of ringed birds are communicated to those individuals and home or foreign stations concerned with a particular record.

The whole point of these international co-operative ringing schemes is based on the hope that a good sample of all birds ringed will be recovered subsequently, either by retrapping or by the various accidents of death befalling a wild bird. In actual practice only 4 or 5 per cent of all birds ringed are recovered, and a large proportion of these are nestlings a few days old, whose recapture is likely to be of interest only to the statistical worker on such aspects of bird life as mortality rates and expectation of life. However, in the course of fifty years, and with several hundred thousand birds being newly ringed every year, very large numbers of valuable recovery records are now being published annually.

To my mind a remarkable feature of the scheme is not that so many ringed birds are subsequently recovered, but that their rings are returned from the remotest quarters of the globe. Consider, for example, the incalculable chances against the recovery of so insignificant a small bird as a reed-warbler (*Acrocephalus scirpaceus*), ringed one summer as a nestling in Switzerland and reported from Tojo on the Gold Coast the following winter; or of that of a rosy pastor (*Pastor roseus*) – a starling – ringed in August as a nestling in Hungary and reported the following April from Lahore in Pakistan, nearly 3,000 miles distant. Of special interest is the case of a tern (*Sterna paradisaea*) ringed north of the Arctic Circle on the west coast of Greenland in July and recovered four months later at Durban, South Africa, having migrated over 10,000 miles in less than 12 weeks – the longest recorded migration of a remarkable series of trans-Atlantic migrations by American terns, and the longest migration of any ringed bird.

We are concerned in this paper with new facts established by the ringing scheme. These may be tabulated as:

(1) Precise information concerning breeding grounds and winter-quarters of individuals and geographical races, where before only broad geographical limits were known for species.

(2) More precise details of migratory routes followed be-

tween summer and winter quarters, and proof of topographical regularity : i.e. migration by identical routes in successive years to identical winter-quarters or nesting places.

(3) Data concerning daily rate of migration.

(4) Physiological data peculiar to migrating birds.

(5) Precise details of 'drift' in unfavourable weather and of 'aberrant' migration.

(6) Explanation of oceanic movements of individual sea-birds, and experimental data concerning the navigational ability of migrating birds.

7) A mass of data relating to the length of life of wild birds.

Let us consider these points in order :

(1) *Range of individuals and geographical races.*

To take two familiar examples, we have long been acquainted in Britain with the autumnal immigration from the north of thrushes – notably fieldfares (*Turdus pilaris*) – and of various species of wild geese; but though we knew the geographical breeding range of the thrushes, we could not be certain in what parts of that range our particular immigrants originated. By means of ringing we are now beginning to learn. Fieldfares, for example, are traditionally known as Norwegian thrushes; and tradition is confirmed in so far as of seventeen ringed fieldfares recovered in Britain ten had in fact been ringed in Norway, one as far north as Finmark. Of the remaining seven, however, six had been ringed in Sweden and the seventh in south-west Finland. Possibly many of our wintering fieldfares come from Finland, for a number ringed in Finland have been recovered in Norway when migrating westwards in the autumn; and some may perhaps come from Russia, for Latvian fieldfares have been recovered in the Low Countries.

It is only during the last decade that large numbers of any species of geese have been ringed. The recent introduction by the Severn Wildfowl Trust of a clap-net released by rockets has much accelerated their ringing in this country, and the percentage of recoveries is high – far too high, for the majority of such recoveries are of dead geese shot by wildfowlers. In addition, large numbers of white-fronted geese (*Anser albifrons*) have been ringed on their breeding grounds in Greenland. As a result of the recoveries from this extensive ringing it has been discovered that the white-fronts of Greenland differ somewhat in size and colouring from those breeding in north Europe and Siberia. As 84 per cent of ringed Greenland white-fronts recovered have been shot in Ireland, and with the exception of a handful recovered in Iceland – where they are known only as birds of passage – the only European recoveries outside Ireland have been one in Wales, two in England and ten in Scotland, it is probable that all those Greenland geese wintering on this side of the Atlantic do so in the British Isles.

A remarkable fact, however, is that from these same West Greenland colonies at least one other ringed white-front has migrated to Canada. Similarly, while 90 per cent of ringed Icelandic wigeon (*Mareca penelope*) have been recovered wintering in Europe, 10 per cent have been recovered on the North American seaboard. These instances of whitefronts and wigeon visiting America may, or may not, be examples of *drift,* which will be considered at greater length in Section 5.

Large numbers of white-fronts also winter on the Severn marshes. Of those ringed there, by means of the rocket-net, there have been six significant recoveries, none from Greenland, all from north or east European localities. Three were shot in the last week of May on, or near, their breeding grounds on the Kanin Peninsula and on Kolguev in the Barents Sea. A fourth, however, was recovered early in April south of Kursk, on the north-east border of the Ukraine, when returning to presumed north Siberian breeding grounds, which extend as far east as Taymyr. Although such a route seems extraordinarily circuitous, it has subsequently been confirmed by two more recoveries from south Russia. Pending further exploration, my own view is that there may be an undiscovered breeding ground of white-fronts in the Aralo-Caspian region.

As no ringed Greenland whitefronts have been recovered on the Severn Marshes – though one in Somerset – and very few of this race observed there, and as none of the European or

Siberian race have been shot in Ireland, it seems that there is very little association between the two races in their winter-quarters. So frequent, however, is the occurrence of *abmigration* (see section 5) among such close relatives as the duck that it would not be altogether surprising to learn, at some future date, that a European whitefront had been recovered in Greenland or a Greenland whitefront in Arctic Russia.

(2) *Migration routes*

Ever since ornithologists first speculated on the geographical routes followed by migrating birds, there have been a variety of theories put forward, some advocating migration on a broad front across continents, others channelled migration along coast-lines and through mountain passes. Factual evidence as to precise routes followed is still meagre, but is increasing annually as evidence becomes available from recoveries of birds ringed at coastal observatories – notably the Fair Isle (midway between Orkney and Shetland), the Isle of May in the Firth of Forth, Spurn Head on the Yorkshire coast, Gibraltar Point on the Wash, Cley on the north Norfolk coast, Lundy in the Bristol Channel, and Skokholm off the coast of Wales; while, on the Continent, we may note especially Jaeran in south-west Norway; Gotland, Öland and Rossitten in the Baltic; and above all Heligoland.

Plotting the recovery points of various European species, one notes that autumn migration is predominantly south-west and south, though large numbers of ducks, waders, and crows migrate due west to their winter-quarters in Atlantic Europe. Ringing, however, has brought to light some interesting exceptions. Cuckoos (*Cuculus canorus*) and wood-warblers (*Phylloscopus sibilatrix*), for example, instead of following the usual west coast route south from Britain to winter-quarters in Africa, apparently travel in a south-easterly direction across Europe, for the only recoveries in Europe of British breeding cuckoos and wood-warblers have been in Italy.

A number of wading birds, notably ruffs (*Philomachus pugnax*) and little stints (*Calidris minuta*), together with some turnstones (*Arenaria interpres*) and sanderling (*Crocethia alba*) also migrate direct across Europe to the Mediterranean, instead of following the west coast route. But the most remarkable example is that of the white wagtail (*Motacilla alba*), another passerine; for while those wagtails breeding in Iceland and Faeroe, the Low Countries, Denmark, and Germany, winter in south and west Europe and tropical Africa, those breeding in Scandinavia and Finland migrate in a south-easterly direction across Europe to Asia Minor and Egypt – a fact only determined by the use of rings.

But, whatever route may be followed, the dominant feature of migration is the regularity with which the same route is followed year after year; though many species return home in the spring by a different route to that taken in the autumn. This topographical conservativeness had long been suspected, and has been abundantly confirmed by ringing. Individuals of many species migrating through the trapping yards of Holland, Belgium, and north Italy have regularly been retrapped at the same station when on passage in subsequent years, and often when returning north in the spring. Of four common sandpipers retrapped on autumn passage through an Essex station, one passed through in the second year almost to the day that it had been ringed the previous year. There are some interesting examples, too, of ducks returning to the same winter-quarters. Two goosanders (*Mergus merganser*) wintering on a Surrey reservoir, for example, were retrapped there two and three winters later, six others being recovered on their breeding grounds in Finland, North Russia, and Sweden. There are a large number of instances, too, of ringed birds returning to the same nesting territory and even to the same nest in successive years, especially of swallows (*Hirundo rustica*), martins (*Delichon urbica*), and swifts (*Micropus apus*), often accompanied by the same ringed mates.

Migration is not solely a long-distance movement between summer and winter quarters. It may take the form of a purely local wandering of a few miles after the nesting season. Ringing has provided an immense amount of data as to the nature of these, often random, post-nesting dispersals. Consider, in this respect, the robin (*Erithacus rubecula*).

Of some 2,500 ringed British robins recovered during the past 40 years only twelve have been recovered more than 25 miles from their ringing places. Of those, eight were young birds recovered in their first year within a range of 50 miles, and in varying directions from their birthplace. Such random dispersal is characteristic of the young of many species that are not true long-distance migrants. Even among true migrants, we find that the young terns, for example, often commence their long southern journeys to African coasts in autumn by initially wandering north 100 miles or more.

A typical dispersal of a young robin is illustrated by the record of one I myself ringed in Newtonmore – a village lying at an altitude of 750 feet in Upper Strathspey, Inverness-shire. It was recovered the following winter in Tomnavoulin, another hill village 36 miles *north-east,* as the raven flies, across the Cairngorm foothills, but nearer 100 miles by the route it probably followed, north down Spey and then south-east up the Avon.

Though so few British robins undertake long-distance migrations – in contrast, as in the case of so many passerines, to the great journeys of Continental robins – the inevitable exception is provided by a young robin from Essex, which migrated 500 miles south to reach the Landes in south-west France in its first autumn. Ringing has revealed that a surprising number of individuals of presumed non-migratory species do in fact undertake long migrations.

Definite migrations may also be made other than autumnal movements south or west to winter-quarters or spring returning movements north or east to nesting territories. It had long been known, for example, that large numbers of shelduck (*Tadorna tadorna*) migrated in early autumn to the great tidal flats in the Bight of Heligoland where they moult, returning home from October onwards. The question was where did they come from? Ringing has now proved that some at any rate are British, for breeding shelduck from Fife, the Solway, and Hampshire have all been recovered in the Bight between August and October; while others, ringed during those months in the moulting area, have been recovered on the Wash and Morecambe Bay. (This may be the only occasion when British shelduck emigrate abroad.) Other moulting shelduck in the Bight had previously been ringed in the Baltic, Denmark, and Holland.

(3) *Rate of migration*

Of the daily rate of migration virtually nothing was known in the pre-ringing era, though that very fine naturalist, albeit somewhat wild theorist, Herr Gätke of Heligoland, believed, sixty years ago, that the red-spotted bluethroat (*Luscinia svecica*) habitually migrated 1,600 miles from Africa to Heligoland in 9 hours at a speed of 180 miles per hour! Even today our data on this subject are meagre, for speed records are mainly dependent on a migrant, ringed at one of the coastal observatories, being picked up immediately it alights at its resting place – the majority alighting after a night journey early in the morning.

From such data as are available most passerines appear to migrate at a speed of 50 to 60 miles a day, though this rate must often be exceeded, and perhaps usually is. The fastest recorded migratory passage made by any ringed bird is that of a passerine, a wheatear (*Oenanthe oenanthe*). Though seldom flying more than a score or two of yards in its breeding territory, the wheatear is a strong flyer, one race habitually migrating from Greenland to North Africa. The wheatear in question was ringed as an adult on Skokholm on 16 August and was picked up 43 hours later at Capbreton on the coast of the Landes in south-west France, and must therefore have covered this stage of its migration at a minimum speed of 335 miles per day: i.e. if it travelled by the most direct route straight across the Bay of Biscay. More probably it followed the French coast-line, and therefore actually covered a greater daily mileage.

The second fastest recorded long-distance flight was not a normal migration, but was the result of an experiment on homing carried out by G. V. T. Matthews. Another Skokholm bird, in this case a sea-bird, a Manx shearwater (*Puffinus puffinus*), was transported across the Atlantic in an aeroplane to

Boston, Mass. Released there, it covered the 3,300 miles return journey to Skokholm at a speed of about 250 miles a day. With this long-distance record may be compared that of a turnstone, which was ringed while on autumn passage through Jaeran in south-west Norway, and was recovered three weeks later at Dakar in Senegal, and must therefore have migrated not less than 3,500 miles at a minimum rate of 175 miles a day. Fast passages are a feature of wader migration; a common sandpiper, ringed on the Essex coast on 17 May, was recovered in the south of Norway four days later, having travelled at not less than 160 miles a day. This rate has been exceeded by another small passerine, a blue-headed wagtail (*Motacilla flava*), which migrated in September from Belgium to Lisbon at a minimum speed of 170 miles per day. As more data become available, it is reasonable to suppose that considerably faster migrations than any of these will be recorded – though none is likely to approach Gätke's bluethroat!

(4) *Weight changes in migrating birds*

During the past year or two coastal trapping stations have initiated research into the physiological changes that take place in a migrating bird, particularly in regard to loss of weight. (Weighing, incidentally, is also useful as a means of differentiating between geographical races, as there are often well-marked differences in minimum and maximum weights between two races, though usually also a number of indeterminate borderline cases.) At Fair Isle, where intensive study of bird weights has been conducted since the war, an accumulating mass of data indicates that during the comparatively short passage across the North Sea, from Norway or the Skagerrak to Shetland, migrant passerines commonly lose 20 to 30 per cent of their weight, even if the crossing is made under favourable weather conditions, but that they quickly put on weight after arrival on Fair Isle. This discovery has been made possible by the frequency with which many migrant birds are retrapped at intervals after their initial ringing on the Island. An immigrant hedge-sparrow (*Prunella modularis*), for example, increased its arrival weight on Fair Isle by 30 per cent in 13 days, and by 45 per cent in 26 days. In a prolonged *drift,* therefore, the loss of weight must be high, and it will be apparent that such drift must lead to heavy mortality from starvation among migrants.

(5) *Drift and abmigration*

Intensive study of ringed birds recovered at coastal stations, coupled with observation of migration actually in progress and of associated weather conditions, has revealed that an immense amount of off-course drifting takes place in unfavourable weather conditions, particularly among those species that migrate mainly during the hours of darkness. Such drifting explains the many records of 'rare' birds and of others reported hundreds or thousands of miles off their normal course – such instances as that of a Dutch cormorant, *Phalacrocorax carbo* (normally migrating no farther than North Africa), recovered on the Great Lakes in North America two years after ringing; or of a young black-headed gull, *Larus ridibundus,* from Yorkshire (normally wintering no farther south than Spain), recovered wintering in the Azores; or of a young gull-billed tern, *Gelochelidon nilotica,* from Denmark (normally wintering in Africa), recovered in the Barbados in its first autumn; or of a Caspian tern, *Hydroprogne caspia,* ringed as a nestling on the shores of Lake Michigan and recovered twelve years later on the coast of Yorkshire. The last is a particularly striking instance of the value of ringing, for there is a European race of Caspian terns inhabiting Sweden and Finland, which have been recorded only as vagrants in the British Isles. This specimen would therefore certainly have been added to the list of European vagrants, had it not borne an American ring.

The classic example of drift, however, is that of a flock of lapwings (*Vanellus vanellus*), which left Cumberland for Ireland, it is supposed, soon after dusk on the evening of 19 December 1927, but overshot their landfall, with a 55-m.p.h. easterly gale behind them, and ultimately came to rest on the shores of Newfoundland. None, of course, survived to create a colony of American lapwings, and their origin would have been unknown had not one borne a ring, with which it had been banded as a nestling, two summers earlier, on the shores of Ullswater in Cumberland.

More recently there have been some interesting examples of drift among migrating passerines. Seven redwings (*Turdus musicus*), which had been ringed while on passage through, or wintering in, this country, have subsequently been recovered abroad. Of these, three ringed while wintering in the West Country, and a fourth trapped in December at Gibraltar Point on the Wash, were recovered in subsequent winters in various parts of Italy; presumably the normal winter-quarters of these particular redwings. That they had previously wintered in Britain was therefore probably the result of a westerly drift off-course. The possible breeding grounds of these off-course redwings are indicated by the fact that of other redwings recovered in Italy, four had been ringed in Finland, a fifth at Rossitten (at the extreme south of the Baltic) and two more in north Sweden and north Norway.

Consider also that immense influx of Continental robins – probably from Norway and Sweden, possibly from Finland or even farther north-east – which reached the East Coast of Britain in October 1951, when large numbers were ringed at coastal trapping stations. From those ringed at Spurn Head in Yorkshire and Cley on the north Norfolk coast a notable series of four recoveries were subsequently obtained: one being recovered later the same winter in Castellon on the east coast of Spain, two on Minorca, and one at Leghorn on the north-west coast of Italy. Although one of the four was not ringed at Spurn until 1 October, it had reached Leghorn, considerably more than 1,000 miles distant by any possible route it may have followed, and had corrected its drift westwards, as early as 12 November. These robins, therefore, bound for winter-quarters in the Mediterranean – and possibly in North Africa, where recoveries have been made of robins ringed as far north as the Baltic Islands – passed through the British Isles only as a result of drift.

Not all rare vagrants are the result of drift. Some are the fore-runners of large-scale irruption by such species as crossbills

(*Loxia curvirostra*) or waxwings (*Bombycilla garrulus*) migrating far beyond their normal range in years when their food supply has failed. Others herald an extension of a species' geographical range, as in the recent case of the Indian collared dove (*Streptopelia decaocto*), which since 1900 has spread in a north-westerly direction across Europe from breeding grounds in Bulgaria and Albania, colonizing one country after another, finally arriving in England in 1952, though not yet recorded breeding here.

Others are the result of 'abmigration' – a phenomenon particularly common among waders and ducks. Abmigration occurs when a bird (usually a young one), bred in this country and wintering here, accompanies foreigners which have also wintered here to *their* home countries in the spring, instead of returning to its own British nesting grounds. Thus there are no fewer than six records of British-ringed woodcock (*Scolopax rusticola*) abmigrating. These six records actually represent 40 per cent of all British-bred woodcock recovered on the Continent, for nearly three-quarters of our native birds are resident throughout the year in these islands. Of these six, one young bird bred in Perthshire was recovered in Norway the following May, while no fewer than three Irish adults, together with a fourth from Hampshire, were recovered in Sweden in April or May. One of the Irish woodcock was in its seventh summer, and it seems remarkable that such an old bird should abmigrate. Even more remarkable perhaps is the sixth record – that of a Kirkcudbrightshire woodcock recovered as far east as the province of Moscow in its third summer.

Among ducks, a wigeon, bred on Loch Leven in Kinross, was recovered at Lake Ilmen in west Russia in its third autumn; while a second from the Solway district was taken in its third summer on the Siberian Pechora (65° N.; 53° E.) – more than 30 per cent of foreign wigeon recovered wintering in Britain having been ringed on breeding grounds in Russia or Siberia. It would be interesting to discover whether these British abmigrants breed in their foreign stations, for the vast majority of our native wigeon are resident in these islands.

Abmigration is not common among passerines: but there is

one record of a swallow, which was ringed as a nestling on the Isle of Man and recovered two summers later in the Driva district of Norway. Presumably this swallow had got 'caught up' with Norwegian swallows at some point on its spring migration north, when returning from winter-quarters in South Africa, where more than twenty British ringed swallows have been reported.

(6) *Oceanic movements of sea birds*

Without some form of individual marking it is almost impossible to ascertain what happens to those species of sea-birds that winter at sea. Do they merely wander about offshore or make trans-oceanic migrations to traditional fishing grounds? Ringing is producing good dividends with sea-birds, though the percentage of recoveries is inevitably small among pelagic species. However, ten kittiwake gulls (*Rissa tridactyla*), ringed as nestlings on British cliffs, have subsequently been recovered on the Grand Banks off Newfoundland – those incomparable fishing banks – with, in addition, an eleventh off Labrador and two more off the west coast of Greenland, one as far north as the Davis Strait. One had crossed the Atlantic less than eight weeks after fledging. The full significance of these records becomes apparent, when it is found that they represent about 40 per cent of all those kittiwakes recovered at any distance from their ringing cliffs. So large a percentage suggests very strongly that there is a regular annual trans-Atlantic migration of a proportion of British kittiwakes – mainly the younger birds – to traditional fishing grounds off the North American coast.

Such a migration is probably also common to other British sea-birds. Two young puffins (*Fratercula arctica*), for example, which had been ringed on St Kilda within six days of one another in August, were recovered on the Grand Banks the following December on consecutive days. This latter record suggests, further, that these young puffins had migrated together across the Atlantic. Ringed on St Kilda also were two young fulmars (*Fulmarus glacialis*), one of which was recovered 235 miles east of Newfoundland in November, and the other 100 miles off the coast the following June – for many of these young sea-birds may remain one or two years at sea before returning to nest on their native cliffs.

The larger gulls come into a different category, as mainly in-shore species; but the European lesser black-backs (*Larus fuscus*) make a definite migration to winter-quarters in, or on the coasts of, Africa. On plotting the autumn and winter recoveries of ringed black-backs we make the exciting discovery that, whereas Sardinia and Algeria represent the most easterly limit of recoveries for black-backs migrating south to winter-quarters in West Africa from Faeroe, Norway, Holland, and the British Isles, a proportion of those from Sweden, the island of Bornholm, and Finland follow a south-easterly course across central Europe or south Russia into the Tunis–Tripoli area, the Black Sea, and the Nile Delta south to Victoria Nyanza. Only a proportion, however, do this: for of eighteen long-distance recoveries of black-backs ringed at the Bornholm colony, three were located in West Africa. As in the case of duck and geese, so here, again, we find that phenomenon of birds from the same breeding colony migrating to winter-quarters hundreds of thousands of miles apart; for while some duck from a breeding ground in eastern Siberia will migrate west to winter in the British Isles, others from the same breeding ground migrate south to winter in northern and central India!

Ringing sea-birds has provided the most recent and informative data concerning a migrant bird's powers of navigation, though not the mechanics of this. Notable among such experiments have been those of R. M. Lockley and others with Manx shearwaters breeding on Skokholm. Though, like other shearwaters, a bird of powerful flight, the Manx is seldom observed more than 200 miles out in the Atlantic, and although there have been nearly 2,000 recoveries of shearwaters ringed on Skokholm, only one, as recently as 1951, has been recovered wintering further afield than the Bay of Biscay – this exception being a young bird ringed on Skokholm in the second week of September and recovered at Rio de Janeiro ten weeks later. The fact that so few have been observed at any distance offshore makes more remarkable the results obtained by transporting nesting adults, and also non-breeding shearwaters, to a distance from Skokholm and then releasing them. Thus, one Skokholm shearwater released at Start Point in south Devon, 220 miles distant as the crow flies (but not the shearwater), was back in its nesting burrow on Skokholm within ten hours. (Two Skokholm puffins, released at the same point, took five days to return to their burrows.) Two other shearwaters, released at an inland station in Surrey, were back on the island the next day; while a non-breeding bird released in Worcestershire returned within five days: in contrast to the record of another non-breeding bird, which did not return to the island until the following May. From further afield two Skokholm shearwaters released in the Faeroe Isles covered the 700 miles back to Skokholm in 11 and 12 days respectively. (A Faeroese shearwater, with a nestling, took 32 days to return to Faeroe from its point of release in the Firth of Forth.) An interesting contrast is afforded by two other Skokholm shearwaters, one with a nestling and the other with an egg, released on the Isle of May in the Firth of Forth: the former homing in 11 days, the latter in 27 days. From the French coast one released at Le Havre in April took 29 days to return to Skokholm, while another released from Cape Finistère in north-west Spain in July did not return until the following May.

Thus far we have been considering homing records from within the Manx shearwater's specific, if not individual, geographical range – though they do not of course normally fly overland. But, in addition, there are a number of experimental homing records from localities where no Manx shearwater has ever been known to occur – first, two records of Skokholm birds released at Venice, 930 miles as the crow flies, or 3,700 miles by sea, from Skokholm. In one instance the bird was back in its burrow within 14 days of its release: the other did not return until the following spring. Then, of three released in Switzerland, one returned from Berne in 13 days, and two from Lugano in 15 and 18 days respectively. The records I have cited, together with that trans-Atlantic flight from Boston, are of course of successful homers: others never returned to Skokholm; but these ringing experiments demonstrate conclusively that wherever it may be – in its nesting territory, its winter-quarters, or at some point between the two – a bird is always in a state of fixed relation to those points on the earth's surface representing nesting territory and winter-quarters, and can often reorientate itself, though carried hundreds of miles off its course during drift in unfavourable air-currents. At this stage no more can be said. We have no conception, for example, of how a young cuckoo – whose parents emigrate from the breeding quarters weeks before their offspring – can find its way to winter-quarters in Africa of whose very existence it has no knowledge.

(7) *Length of life*

Though investigation into a bird's length of life is a secondary issue of the ringing scheme, an immense amount of data is now available from recovery records, and it appears that the average expectation of life of passerine nestlings ranges, according to species, from one to two and a half years. That expectation of life, however, bears no relation to potential longevity is indicated by the record of one redwing, which was ringed while wintering in Belgium in 1931 and recovered in October *nineteen* years later in the Basses-Pyrénées on the Franco-Spanish frontier. Other records of long life, which would have been considered fabulous without the proof of rings, include those of a goldfinch (*Carduelis carduelis*) ringed while wintering in Germany in 1931 and recovered sixteen years later wintering 300 miles distant in Belgium; and of a meadow-pipit (*Anthus pratensis*) ringed on its first autumn passage through Holland and recovered in the south of Norway thirteen years later in November. Larger birds live to a potentially greater age. Many gulls and some terns have been recovered more than twenty years after ringing; though I have not traced any older than a German oystercatcher (*Haematopus ostralegus*) recovered twenty-three years after being ringed as a nestling.

FURTHER READING

Deelder, C. L. 1949. *On the Autumn Migration of the Scandinavian Chaffinch.* Leiden.

Simms, Eric. 1952. *Bird migrants. Some aspects and observations.* London: Cleaver-Hume Press Ltd.

Williamson, K. 1952. Migrational drift in Britain in Autumn 1951. *Scottish Naturalist,* Vol. 64, No. 1.

Wynne-Edwards, V. C. 1935. On the Habits and Distribution of Birds on the North Atlantic. *Proc. of the Boston Soc. of Nat. Hist.,* Vol. 40, No. 4, p. 233–346.

SEEING'S BELIEVING

M. L. JOHNSON

Photogravure illustrations between pp. 64 *and* 65

SEEING seems to be an effortless process. You are not aware of doing any hard work, or of exercising any skill, in distinguishing your mother from your father, a square from a circle, in recognizing that your nose is closer to your eye than your foot is, or a tree-top nearer than the moon. 'The perceptual act is not an *activity*. There is in it no element of fussiness, no wondering or questioning, one does not have to take trouble over it – it is a blessed relief from the labour of discursive thought' (Price, 1932).

As a matter of fact, however, each of us has had to *learn* to see ordinary things, to develop and exercise a skill of seeing. Most of us did this in infancy as a part of natural development, and we have forgotten how much effort it cost us. A two-and-a-half-year-old child 'may sometimes look with such overpowering intensity that his legs collapse under him' (Gesell, Ilg, and Bullis, 1949). Studies of adult people congenitally blind because of cataract, who were able to see after operation, have shown that learning to see is for them an extraordinarily complex and laborious process. It took at least a month for a patient to learn to see even a small number of objects as other people see them. After thirteen days of training, a patient could not say what was the difference between a square and a triangle without counting the corners. Although a cube of sugar could be correctly named when seen on the table, it was not recognized when suspended by a thread against a different background (Senden, 1932, quoted Hebb, 1949).

Some experiments on chimpanzees reared in darkness up to the age of 16 months also demonstrated the need for prolonged apprenticeship in seeing. Apart from eye reflexes, which were normal, the animals behaved as though they were blind for some time after they had been brought into daylight. For instance, if the nipple of a feeding bottle touched the hand or face, it was immediately seized in the mouth, but there was no sign of visual recognition of it until the thirty-third meal taken on the eleventh day after the animal had been brought into daylight (Riesen, 1947).

Let us enquire a little further into how we have learnt to reduce the effort of seeing. We are well aware that we do not take notice of the whole 'stimulus pattern' (the image that falls on the retina), but select from it. Haldane (1937) when he put on Mr Leakey's cap of darkness to make himself invisible said that 'everything looked slightly odd, and at first I couldn't think why. Then I saw that the two ghostly noses which I always see without noticing them were gone.' We ignore those parts of the stimulus pattern which are not at the moment useful, and pay attention to others. Different people, or the same person at different times, presented with the same stimulus pattern, will see different things according to their interests and present needs. Children are often thought to be specially observant – 'they notice everything' – because they tend to comment on things at random, less according to any canalized interest. We save ourselves trouble by learning which parts of a familiar stimulus pattern we can afford to ignore, and which we must pay attention to; thus we see more easily if we know what to expect. Waiting in a bus queue we can distinguish the number of an approaching bus at a much greater distance if we know which numbers are likely to come along the road. We come to the perceptual act with a mind prepared. Bartlett wrote:

Certain of the tendencies which the subject brings with him into the situation with which he is called upon to deal are utilized so as to make his reaction the 'easiest' or the least disagreeable, or the quickest and least obstructed that is at the time possible. When we try to discover how this is done, we find that always it is by an effort to connect what is given with something else. Thus, the immediately present 'stands for' something not immediately present, and 'meaning', in the psychological sense, has its origin. As we have seen, in certain cases of great structural simplicity, or of structural regularity, or of extreme familiarity, the immediate data are at once fitted to, or matched with, a perceptual pattern which appears to be pre-existent so far as the particular perceptual act is concerned. This pre-formed setting, scheme, or pattern is utilized in a completely unreflecting, unanalytical, and unwitting manner. Because it is utilized, the immediate perceptual data have meaning, can be dealt with, and are assimilated. (F. C. Bartlett, *Remembering,* 1932, Cambridge University Press.)

This way of behaving makes the seeing of, noticing of, reacting to, familiar things which can fit into a pre-existent perceptual scheme quick and easy, but it has the disadvantage that one tends to overlook discrepancies between the stimulus pattern and the perceptual scheme, and see things not as they really are, but as one expects them to be. Many experiments have shown how such characteristics as the shape, size, colour, and position of objects are as it were 'projected' on to them by the observer according to his perceptual scheme. For instance, perception of colour and shape depends not only on the thing which is looked at, but partly also on past experience of the colour and shape of similar things. When subjects were momentarily shown playing cards with the colour reversed, e.g. a red six of clubs, some reported normal cards, either a black six of clubs, or red six of diamonds or hearts, others saw them as purple or brown. It seems that rather than see such a monstrosity as a red club, people will change the colour to what it 'ought' to be – black – or will compromise with brown or purple, or they will change the shape to fit the colour and call a club a diamond or heart (Bruner and Postman, 1949).

Some of the most remarkable experiments are those designed by Ames at the Hanover Institute, New Hampshire, U.S.A., which have stimulated a great deal of interest in the problems of perception. When people are shown playing cards of different sizes in an otherwise darkened room, they do not see them as differing in size, but as being at distances which vary inversely with their size. If a normal card, one half as big, and another twice as big, are placed at the same distance, the observer sees them all as normal cards, the small one more distant, the large one nearer, than the normal one. Thus the observer alters the distance at which the cards appear to be placed in order to make all playing cards conform to the standard size he is familiar with. I remember vividly an experience (which I understand is very common) of going behind the scenes after a marionette show and being quite astounded that the wooden puppets were only a foot or so tall; during the play I had seen them as much nearer life size, the size of the people they represented.

One of the most remarkable demonstrations is that of the 'distorted room'. This is a room which when viewed through a peep hole looks like an ordinary symmetrical room with two similar windows at the far side. The observer seems to be looking into the room from the middle of one side (Fig. 1). When other things are brought into the room they look very strange. People appear tiny or gigantic according to which corner they are standing in (Plates 14, 15). A marble rolling across the floor may appear to go uphill. When the observer is asked to try to

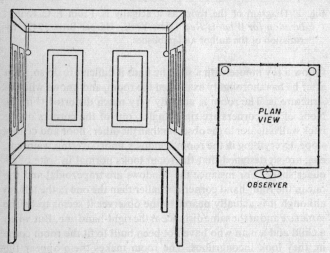

Fig. 1. Diagram of the room as it appears to be. From E. C. Kelley. *Education for What is Real* (New York: Harper Bros, 1947). By permission of the author and publisher.

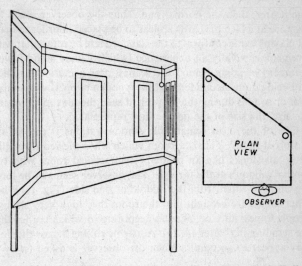

Fig. 2. Diagram of the room as it actually is. From E. C. Kelley. *Education for What is Real* (New York: Harper Bros, 1947). By permission of the author and publisher.

follow a toy mouse with a stick he finds it difficult to do so, even after he has thoroughly examined the room, and knows what its structure is. The room is actually very much distorted (Fig. 2). None of the corners are right angles; one of the corners of the back wall is nearer to the observer than the other; floor and ceiling slope. Everything in the room, windows, floor covering, wainscot, etc., are so designed that the room looks normal in spite of its queer shape. For instance the windows are trapezoidal and the one in the right-hand corner is smaller than the one in the left, so although it is actually nearer to the observer it seems to be the same size and at the same distance as the right-hand one. But when a child and a man who have not been built to fit the room come in, they look incongruous. The room makes them appear the same distance away, whichever corner they stand in, and so they look larger in the right-hand (near) corner than in the left, more distant one. But why is it that the people who are normal look

1. A mature coconut plantation in Ceylon.

2. A nursery of young coconut palms. It should be noted that the juvenile leaves are of simpler form than those on the mature palms, a common phenomenon among plants.

3. Replanting (underplanting) an old coconut plantation.

4. A newly opened coconut inflorescence.

5. Three stages in the development of the coconut inflorescence. Left to right: (*a*) newly opened as in plate 4; (*b*) male flowers partly shed; (*c*) male flowers all shed, female flowers ('button nuts') remaining.

6. Crown of a mature coconut palm with one inflorescence bagged for artificial pollination.

(Photos for Plates 1–6 R. Child).

7. Effects of drought on a coconut plantation in Ceylon (*photo O.B.M. Cheyne*).

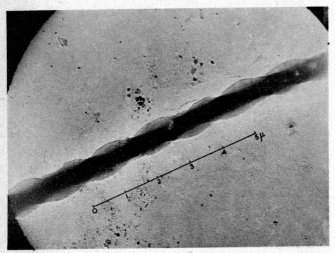

8. Electronmicrograph of part of the tail of a *Limnaea* sperm from a dextral individual; the spiral is coiled dextrally (i.e. in the same direction as a carpenter's screw). Not fixed, shadowed with gold-palladium at 40° (see p.121).

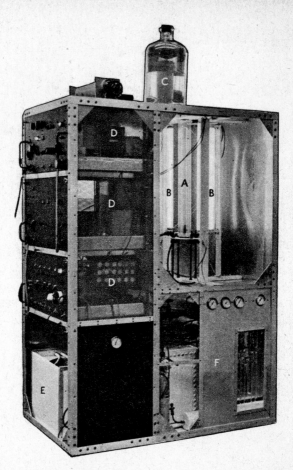

9. Automatic apparatus for the continuous culture of *Chlorella* under constant conditions. In this apparatus a photo-electric device admits fresh medium into the culture as it grows, at such a rate that the concentration of cells is maintained at a constant value. Portions of the culture may be withdrawn aseptically at intervals and used for experimental purposes. A, culture tube; B, 2 ft. fluorescent lamps; C, medium reservoir; D, electrical control apparatus for cell concentration, light intensity, temperature and aeration; E, thermostat tank; F, Flowmeters and reservoirs for air and carbon dioxide. *Reference, Myers and Clark, J. Gen. Physiol.*, 1944, **28**, 103–112; *photo R. Brinsden.*

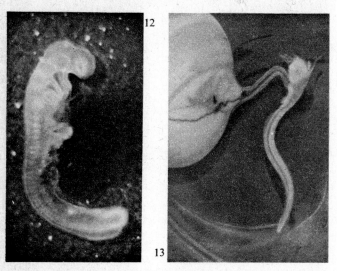

10. The rough dogfish, *Scyliorhinus canicula*. (× about ¼).

11. The spiny dogfish *Squalus acanthias*. Plates 10 and 11 from Joubin, by permission of Andr. Høst et Fils, Copenhagen. (× about 1/10).

12. A living dogfish embryo, two months old. Three open gill slits have developed; just behind these is the cut end of the stalk attaching the embryo to the yolk sac. (× about 8).

13. Part of a cinematograph film showing a headless dogfish embryo swimming attached to its yolk sac. (× about 2).

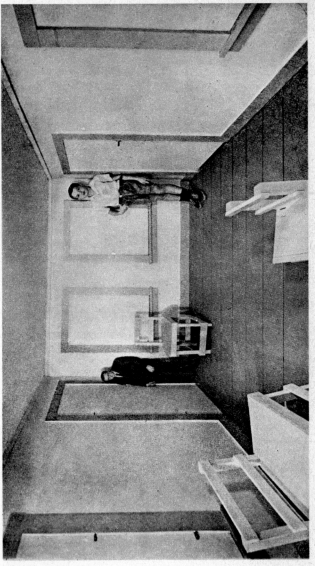

14. The distorted room (see pp. 63–4).

15. The distorted room (see pp. 63-4). *Both courtesy Life International. Copyright Time Inc. 1950.*

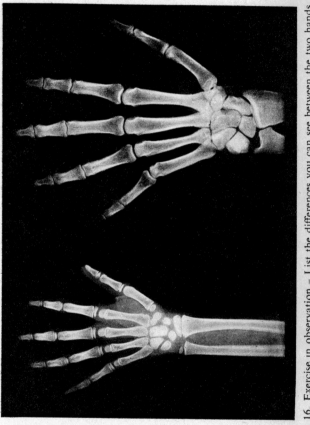

16. Exercise in observation – List the differences you can see between the two hands (see pp. 71–73). *Courtesy* The Lancet.

wrong? Why does their presence not make the observer see the room for what it is, distorted? A likely explanation is that we want to keep our environment stable so that we can move about with surety, and when we are forced to admit incongruity we prefer to see it in movable objects like people rather than in static ones like rooms. Thus we interpret the stimulus pattern in terms of our past experience and present and future needs. To quote Ames (1951), 'these interpretations do not occur at the conscious level, rather they are unconscious, and may be characterized as *assumptions* as to the probable significance of indications received from the environment'. The makers of practical jokes for Christmas parties depend for their success on this mode of behaviour. The shock of biting into a cream bun made of rubber with a squeak in it is the shock of discovering that our assumptions as to the probable significance of the indications received from the bun have been wrong. As we go through life we are continually, but more or less unconsciously, testing our assumptions by acting on them, and, more or less unconsciously, we modify them according to our experience. Consequently, if we see things often enough we learn to see them reliably.

The difficulty is with seeing new things. Let us be quite clear, however, that newness is only a relative matter; we recognize the table in our living-room as a stable, persisting object, although its retinal image differs according to our own position relative to it (just as photographs of it vary with the position of the camera); the stimulus pattern changes with the slightest movement of our head or eye, with the passing of a cloud, the flicker of the fire. We recognize it as the same table whether it is bare, or whether part of its surface is obscured by a book. Our perceptual scheme of the table is flexible enough to accept such differences in the stimulus patterns received from the table; it has been made so because similar differences have been experienced in the past. Sometimes, however, the discrepancies between stimulus pattern and perceptual scheme are not so easily reconciled. My son, at the age of four, after playing for the first time with a little black girl, said she was very nice, but, screwing up his eyes with intense effort, 'I can't quite see her.' Hebb's experiments (1946) indicate that the fear that apes show of a mutilated face or a dead monkey is due to the inability to match the new thing with the perceptual scheme: the new thing is sufficiently like the expected to be reminiscent of it, but sufficiently unlike to be recognized as incongruous and therefore frightening.

We are often faced with things that are so new, so different from things experienced in the past that they cannot be fitted or forced into our perceptual scheme. We then feel that we have difficulty in understanding them, and get confused. As G. H. Lewes (1879) most beautifully put it, 'And the new object presented to Sense, or the new idea presented to Thought, must also be *soluble in old experiences,* be *re*-cognized as like them, otherwise it will be unperceived, uncomprehended.' The reaction often shown to some examples of modern art illustrates this. The layman is puzzled by a painting by Paul Klee or Ben Nicolson, and asks 'But what does it mean?' a question which tends to irritate the art connoisseur, who already knows what it means (i.e. he can fit it into his perceptual scheme) even if he avers that 'paintings don't have to mean anything'.

Recent work on the nature of perception has profoundly influenced thinking about man's behaviour (see, for instance, Kelley, Cantril), and it is tempting to consider further some of its wider implications. In this article, however, we shall restrict our attention mainly to the implications it has for the understanding of some of the problems of observation in biology.

OBSERVATION IN BIOLOGY

Many of the facts of biology are collected by looking at plants and animals. The biologist must observe as far as possible accurately and not distort what he sees in order to fit the stimulus pattern into his perceptual scheme – he must be able to see red clubs as red clubs. As far as possible he must not select from the stimulus pattern only those parts which fit in with his preconceptions, ignoring other things which might contradict them (I say 'as far as possible', because the observations can never be independent of the observer). He must be able to see new, un-expected things. Developing skill in accurate and comprehensive observation is therefore an important part of the training of a biologist.

I suppose most biologists can remember the sense of floundering bewilderment experienced on first looking down a microscope, at, say, a prepared section of kidney. The novice is in the same position as one of Senden's patients opening his eyes to a world of shapes, sizes and colours, that as yet mean nothing to him. In this unfamiliar, complicated, almost featureless muddle, it seems impossible to distinguish what is significant and what irrelevant. 'But what am I *supposed* to see?' the student asks, and this irritates the teacher, just as 'What does it mean' irritates the art connoisseur. The question puts the teacher in a dilemma. On the one hand he wants to help his pupils to learn what a kidney section looks like, i.e. to tell them what they are supposed to see, to give them a perceptual scheme of it, on the other hand he wants to train them to make unbiassed observations, to see what is there, and he knows only too well the dangers of telling them what they are *supposed* to see. They tend to see what they expect to see, whether it is there or not; and they tend not to see things that are there, if they do not expect to see them.

It is extraordinarily difficult for students to distinguish between what is there and what they think ought to be there, as any teacher or examiner and any introspective student will know. In an examination for first year University students the orthodox question 'Identify and write illustrated notes on A' was set ('A' being a transverse section of *Hydra*). Most of the candidates who identified the section correctly made drawings which were much more like text-book diagrams than the real thing. This might be due to the difficulties of drawing realistically, but this explanation is unlikely because of the students who failed to identify the section correctly relatively twice as many made good illustrations. Indeed the best illustration of all was in this group. The more likely explanation, and one that fits in with a lot of other experience, is that if the student has decided that the specimen is a section of *Hydra* and finds no reason to doubt it, he tends to draw the diagram in his mind's eye rather than the section under the microscope. In Bartlett's words, 'the immediate data are at once fitted into, or matched with, a perceptual pattern which appears to be pre-existent'. On the other hand, the student who gets the identification wrong, and therefore discovers contradictory things in the section, finds it more difficult to match it to his mind's eye diagram, takes more trouble over it, and succeeds in making a more realistic picture.

We must look a little more closely into the function of the diagram and its effects on observation. A diagram may be compared with a perceptual scheme which has not been made by the student, but has been borrowed. It resembles a perceptual scheme in that it is not a picture of any one section, but a highly schematized representation of a kind of average or mean of many sections, and in that certain aspects only have been selected for representation. The most striking way in which a diagram differs from a photograph is in its simplicity. Most things ('irrelevant details') have been left out so that a few 'significant' things are made clear. Significant and irrelevant in relation to what? In relation to the observer's needs (as in a perceptual scheme) – to what is thought suitable for the student to learn about *Hydra,* which biological principles it can usefully illustrate. Usually *Hydra* is studied as a 'type' of animal with only two layers of cells in its body wall. The diagram, like a perceptual scheme which you have made yourself, helps you to see *Hydra* as an animal with two cellular layers in its body wall; the trouble is it tends to stop you seeing anything else, and any preconceptions as to what the thing ought to look like, any instructions as to what to look for, tend to have this dual effect, of both assisting and inhibiting observation. This is the dilemma of learning, and teaching, to be observant.

It is not only beginners in biology who see things that are not there and fail to see things that are; practised observers also make these errors, according to their assumptions. For more than thirteen centuries it was believed (even by acute observers such as Leonardo) that the septum between the ventricles of the heart is perforated. The presence of pores was demanded by Galen's theory of the function of the heart which required that blood should pass through the septum. At last Vesalius in 1543 questioned the existence of the pores: 'The septum is formed from the very densest substance of the heart, it abounds on both sides with pits. Of these none, so far as the senses can perceive, penetrate from the right to the left ventricle; we wonder at the art of the Creator which causes blood to pass from right to left ventricle through invisible pores.' Twelve years later, in the second edition of his book, he is firmer: 'Not long ago, I would not have dared to turn aside even a hair's breadth from Galen, but it seems to me that the septum of the heart is as thick, dense, and compact as the rest of the heart. I do not see, therefore, how even the smallest particle can be transferred from the right to the left ventricle through the septum.' (Singer, 1950.)

The error of failing to see things that are there is exemplified by the following story. A child with a persistent cough had its throat x-rayed for diagnosis. The radiologist reported that there was nothing in the radiograph to show why the child was coughing. The cough persisted, and the child returned to have another radiograph taken. This time the shadow of a button was seen in the throat region; the button was removed and the child stopped coughing. When the first radiograph was re-examined the shadow of the button was seen there too, but it had been explained away by the radiologist, who had supposed that the child had been x-rayed with its vest on. The radiologist had failed to see the significance of the button for the problem in hand – diagnosis of the cause of the cough – because another explanation for its presence seemed more probable. After all most people wear their buttons outside and not inside their throats.

In biological observation then, as in seeing in ordinary life, the stimulus pattern is interpreted, not simply received; and the interpretations are made according to preconceptions which are only partly if at all recognized. It is possible that a detailed naturalistic study of how biologists observe might help us to understand more about the processes involved, and to gain better control of them. An attempt has been made to do this with medical students, and some account of it will now be given.

I will first attempt to clarify some of the concepts we shall find useful. The term *'stimulus pattern'* following Ames (1951) means the image which falls on the retina; it can be imitated by suitable optical arrangements of lenses and screens modelled on the eye. We will use the term *'perceptual pattern'* for what the subject sees, perceives, observes, notices or reacts to, in any one stimulus pattern; it cannot be imitated optically because seeing involves selection. A perceptual pattern can be regarded as the *information* the subject gets from the stimulus pattern. The perceptual pattern is the result of the interaction of the stimulus pattern with the subject's *'frame of reference'*, defined by Sherif and Cantril (1945) as 'the functionally related factors (past and present) which operate at the moment to determine the particular properties of a psychological phenomenon – perception or judgement for instance'. An important part of the frame of reference is the subject's *perceptual scheme* relating to the present stimulus pattern. *'Perceptual scheme'* will be used for Bartlett's 'pre-formed setting, scheme or pattern', a kind of average or mean of previously experienced similar perceptual patterns. The frame of reference is however very complicated and far-reaching. It includes many factors whose relevance to the stimulus pattern may seem very remote. In the case of Vesalius investigating the structure of the heart, an important factor was his fear of 'departing a hair's breadth from Galen'.

The case of the radiologist diagnosing the child's cough can be used to illustrate these concepts. The stimulus pattern given by the first radiograph included the shadow of a button, but the radiologist's perceptual pattern of it did not. His perceptual pattern was not *significantly* different from his perceptual scheme of healthy throat radiographs, i.e. he got no information as to the cause of the cough. On seeing the second radiograph, his frame of reference had changed, so that he could now entertain the possibility that a button could be inside a throat, and his new perceptual pattern could approximate more closely to the stimulus pattern. As a result of this experience his perceptual scheme of throat radiographs would become modified.

This serves as an example of how scientists work and learn their skill. We may say that the skilful observer is one whose frame of reference is such that he can see significant or meaningful differences between his perceptual schemes and the stimulus patterns he is examining, so that his perceptual patterns approximate more and more closely to the stimulus patterns, and consequently he gets more information out of them. He can see more comprehensively because he can become aware of the possible relationships to his interests of apparently unrelated things.

Thus a study of what goes on when medical students observe involved an investigation of their frames of reference. As we have seen we are personally unaware of many of the factors in our frame of reference, so a special technique is necessary to discover them. The technique used was that of 'free group discussion', originally developed as a teaching technique. In this the students were encouraged to talk very freely about their reactions to a stimulus pattern, so that their frames of reference can be investigated. A detailed account of the situation is necessary in order to make the reader's frame of reference as useful as possible.

The students had just started on their preclinical course, after having studied biology for one to three years. As yet they had little or no knowledge of human anatomy. They met in groups of twelve, and at first each student worked individually. He was given a print of two radiographs (Plate 16) and asked to 'List the differences you can see between these two hands.' The kind of activity required here is an example of much of what a biologist has to do, for comparing and contrasting the appearance of things forms the basis of a good deal of biological work. In diagnosis also a doctor is comparing and contrasting certain features of the patient with his perceptual schemes of the normal healthy condition on the one hand and a series of diseased conditions on the other.

A colleague's answer to the question is given (pages 72 and 73) as a guide to the reader. The students had not yet had practice in setting out information in a schematic form and as

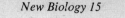

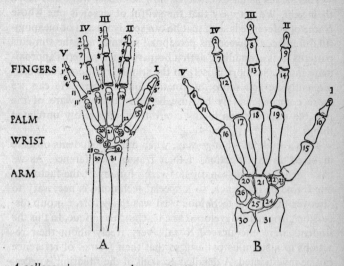

FINGERS

PALM

WRIST

ARM

A   B

A colleague's answer to the exercise 'List the differences you can see between these two hands'

A and B are tracings of the outlines of the white shadows (bones) seen in the x-ray images on the photograph (Plate 16). The comparable rays of bone shadows (fingers and palm) on each tracing have been numbered in roman figures I–V inclusive. The bone image outlines on tracing A have been numbered consecutively 1–31 inclusive. The bone shadows on tracing B judged to correspond in relative position with those on tracing B have been given the same numbers.

Comparison shows:

1. The corresponding bone images are smaller in A than in B.

2. The bone outlines labelled 1′–14′ in A are not present in tracing B.

3. The spaces between the bone outlines are larger in most cases in A than in B. In B these spaces are entirely absent in some regions, the bone outlines overlapping.

4. The bone shadows in the wrist region of A are discrete from each

other (with the exception of 22 and 23). There are 10 shadows (or 9 if 22 and 23 are one). They are simple in shape and homogeneous in whiteness. In B they are close together, angular and heterogeneous in whiteness. It is difficult to trace the outlines in B with certainty; there might be only six.

5. A diffuse shadowing between the bone shadows (flesh) is clearly visible in A, but scarcely visible in B.

6. There are many differences in the shape of the outlines of the long bones 1–14, and 30–31, especially at their approximating surfaces.

The identification of the separate bone outlines in A with those in B, particularly in the wrist region, is only possible by interpreting the shadows on the assumption that the pictures represent two normal human hands at different stages of growth. This assumption seems consistent with past experience of radiographs.

Note on the Exercise

The pictures are in fact made from radiographs of the hand of a normal child 7½ years old (A) and a normal adult (B). In the child there are 7 wrist bones (shadows 20–26), the other three shadows in the wrist region being epiphyses of long bones (27 is the epiphysis of 15, the metacarpal of the thumb; 28 that of 30, the ulna, and 29 that of 31, the radius). In the adult these epiphyses have fused with their long bones, so that the equivalents of 27, 28, and 29 of A are not seen as separate shadows in B. In the adult wrist there are 8 bones, an extra centre of ossification having appeared; this bone, not present in the child, overlaps 26 in B, causing the dense shadow. The dense shadow below the thumb in B is also due to the overlapping of two separate bones, equivalent to 22 and 23 of A. (The dense white patch on 20 in B is due to a projection of the bone itself.)

The explanation makes it clear that the pictures are quite difficult to interpret and we did not expect students to be able to do this. We did not expect them even to know what the limits of the wrist are, that for instance in A 28 and 29 belong to the arm region, and 27 to the palm. In fact they usually recognized that 28 and 29 are the epiphyses of the ulna and radius respectively, but regarded 27 as a wrist bone instead of the epiphysis of the metacarpal of the thumb.

might be expected their answers were usually not so well organized as this; they did not, for instance, trace or number the shadows for ease of reference. But there is another difference of greater importance, a difference in the kind of information they gave. It is uncommon for students to make bare precise statements about differences in size, number, shape and distribution of the shadows in the prints, i.e. statements which can be investigated by reference to the prints alone. Such statements (sometimes called 'facts' or 'data') have a high probability of being correct, i.e. they will usually be confirmed by other observers. The students tend to make instead such statements as 'A is a young hand and B an old hand', 'the bones in B have fused', 'A is a live hand, B is a skeleton'. These are statements (sometimes called conclusions, inferences, or interpretations) whose correctness cannot be investigated by reference to the prints alone, because information other than that supplied by the stimulus pattern is used in making them. They have a lower probability of being correct. As we know very well, people do not agree so readily on conclusions as they do on facts, but conclusions are felt to be more interesting and useful, as any reader who has struggled through pages 72 and 73 will agree.

When the students had individually made their lists of the differences between the two hands, they discussed for an hour and a half the statements they had made. To refer back to our definitions, for our purpose we can consider each student as having received the same stimulus pattern (actually this is not the case, because no two prints could be exactly alike, and no two eyes are optically exactly the same). Each student's list was a description of his perceptual pattern, the information he had got from the print. No two students had exactly the same perceptual pattern, because no two frames of reference are the same. By comparing and contrasting the perceptual patterns some of their determinants could be discovered, i.e. we could start to analyse the students' frames of reference.

A few of the main points which arose in the discussions are cited below. The account is based on experience of 23 discussions covering a period of four years. Although the groups differ very much according to the varied personalities of the members, the same problems come up repeatedly, so we can regard certain important factors as common to many students' frames of reference.

When the statement that A is a young hand, B an old hand was discussed, it appeared that this conclusion was arrived at because of the smaller size of A, and the greater number of bones in it. In discussing the first point, it soon became clear that many students had taken for granted that the size of the prints was a sure guide to the relative sizes of the hands themselves. In support of this they said they must have been radiographed side by side on the same plate because there was no dividing line visible. However, others who were more familiar with radiography and photography pointed out that so many things could have been done to the prints that one was not justified in assuming that they were reduced to the same scale, and one could not therefore safely say anything about the relative ages of the hands on the basis of the size of the prints.

In discussing the second point which was held to support the view that A was a younger hand than B, most students felt sure that the smaller number of bones in B had resulted from fusion of certain bones, which were separate in A. For instance, they said that certain long bones had fused with their epiphyses (e.g. 10 with 10′). Many also thought that the small bones in the wrist region of A had fused together in various ways to form the smaller number in B. While most agreed in principle they had some argument as to which bones fuse with which. They disagreed so much over the details that they began to doubt whether they could with certainty match up the bones in the two hands, and sooner or later someone said that perhaps there were more bones in the wrist of B than appeared; the outlines were vague and in parts the shadows were so dense that it was possible that bones overlapped each other. What is interesting is that the idea of fusion so dominated the mind that other possible explanations for the difference in the apparent number of bones were overlooked – for instance the possibility that in B bones overlapped each other, or that some bones had been resorbed during development. In some cases students who actually knew previously that there are eight bones in the adult wrist 'forgot' it in their attempt to use the hypothesis of fusion to explain why only six bones were visible. This is illustrated by the following extract from a tape recording of a discussion. The group had been very much preoccupied with discussing how they thought the wrist bones had fused. I had pointed out the danger of un-critically using the fusion hypothesis and indicated the relevance of this kind of observing to medicine:

STUDENT F. But I knew there were four bones in the top . . . I well . . . I.

STUDENT E. I knew there were eight. . . .

STUDENT S. I knew there were six! (Laughter.)

STUDENT F (he talks very excitedly). I knew there were eight, I mean . . . the one . . . I . . . I. I knew that there were four at the top – the darkest spot, I said that's the pisiform to myself – but the top one – I just completely . . .

STUDENT E. I didn't trouble to count them, you know – I didn't trouble to . . .

STUDENT F. I counted them and *recounted* them.

STUDENT E. I couldn't even count them properly – they didn't seem in the right . . .

STUDENT F. Oh, I wrote eight and then crossed it out and put six.

STUDENT K. If you look a little more closely they seem to be overlapping there – you can see two.

Further consideration of the statement that the bones had fused in B shows that it was an attempt to read into the pictures something about the past history of B and the future of A. It was an attempt to *explain* B in terms of A, to relate them together. It was based on the presupposition that B had passed through a stage represented by A. This implied that the pictures were taken from the same species. The students were predisposed to think that this was the case, because as medical students they were naturally primarily interested in the human and the word 'hand' (not 'paw' or 'forelimb') tends to imply the human, though it may not be restricted to it. When they discussed the matter, but not until, they realized that they did not know enough about forelimbs to be sure that they were both human hands; one or both might be that of a monkey, or even an amphibian or reptile, for all they knew. This underlines the importance of the formulation of instructions as one of the factors which determines observation. If the instruction had been 'List the differences you can see between the two pictures' the students' reaction to the same stimulus pattern would have been different in many respects.

During this analytical discussion it became clear that the statement 'B is an older hand than A' is a conclusion which has been arrived at as a result of picking up a number of clues, calling on past experience and information which is more or less relevant, ignoring the limitations of their knowledge, and inadequately testing hypotheses to estimate the probability of their being correct. The conclusions they had made were not arrived at as a result of a series of logical steps, but swiftly, and almost unconsciously. The validity of the conclusions was usually not enquired into, indeed the process was usually accompanied by a feeling of certainty of being right, and the discussion of different perceptual patterns consequently often became very heated. Of course, often the correct conclusion is arrived at, and then discussion does not change the formulation of the end result, it only brings to light the things involved in getting it. When the wrong conclusion has been reached it is often held very tenaciously. For instance, in most discussions the question arose as to whether the pictures were of right or left hands. I say 'question', but to many people there seems to be no question about it – some felt absolutely certain they were both right hands, others certain they were both left, others that A was a right and B a left, others that A was a left and B a right, some (usually those with experience of photography) that it was impossible to tell. The discussion revolving round this became very excited; even those who at first had no views, or had not considered the point at all, got swept in and took sides. The difficulty seemed to be in adapting to the idea that a radiograph is a shadow, so that it is impossible to tell from these pictures whether the hands were right or left. Some felt that the flesh shadow round the base of the thumb in A was bulging out towards them, so it was a right hand seen from the palm surface. Others thought it bulged away from them, lying below the bone shadows, so it was a left hand seen from the back. The interesting point, however, is that many found it so difficult to accept that it is really not possible to tell. They used the kind of clues we unconsciously use in everyday life to get information about position in space and could not quickly accept the fact that these clues, which in most cases serve us so well, are useless or even misleading in the x-ray world of shadows. They found it difficult to modify their perceptual scheme, because it would require a wholesale recasting of their ideas about perception of space relationships. In just the same way observers of the distorted room find it difficult to reject the clues which make them see the room as normal. Similarly the mediaeval anatomists saw pores in the ventricular septum not only because Galen did, but because their way of thinking about the function of the heart depended on their presence. If they had *not* seen the pores, they would have had to change their ideas about physiology, and, much worse, about the status of Galen and the church that supported him.

There is not space to do justice to the immense complexity and extreme subtlety of 'the functionally related factors (past and present) which operate at the moment to determine the particular properties of a psychological phenomenon' which were demonstrated in these analytical discussions. In following the apparently simple request to list the differences they could see between two hands, students had picked up all sorts of clues, used all sorts of assumptions in a more or less 'unreflecting, unanalytical and unwitting manner'. Conclusions of varying degrees of validity were made as a result of the 'effort after meaning', 'the effort to connect what is given with something else' which Bartlett described as a fundamental characteristic of human behaviour.

In conclusion we may revert to our title and affirm that for most ordinary situations 'Seeing is believing'. It is so because we have *learnt* to see things in a reliable way, to pick up such clues as will enable us to judge sizes, colours, shapes, and distances correctly. From previous experience of the same or similar things we have made assumptions as to the relationships of a stimulus pattern and the 'real thing'. By acting on our assumptions in the ordinary business of life we continually test them and refine them and modify them as is necessary. An assumption which is usually found to be correct becomes a firmly held belief. Our assumptions define and limit what we see, i.e. we tend to see things in such a way that they will fit in with our assumptions even if this involves distortion or omission. We therefore may invert our title and say 'Believing is seeing'.

In science, too, the accuracy and comprehensiveness of seeing depends on our assumptions, beliefs, or attitudes. The scientist is often dealing with unfamiliar things and must always be on the look-out for new things, and what seems to be even more difficult, for new relationships of familiar things. He can do this to the extent that his assumptions or beliefs relating to the subject he is working on are modifiable. This again depends on innumerable interacting factors, many of them unconscious, some of them apparently trivial, others deeply rooted in personality. It is possible that a naturalistic study of how biologists observe might help us to learn how to observe more accurately and comprehensively by making us aware of some of these factors, and subjecting them to what Helmholtz called 'the purifying and scrutinizing work of conscious thinking'.

FURTHER READING

For a clear and concise general introduction to some of the problems of observation see *A further study of visual perception,* by M. D. Vernon, 1952, Cambridge University Press. As far as improving the training of scientists is concerned, some fruitful ideas are those used by workers on the inter-relations of personality and perception. *Perception, an approach to personality,* by R. R. Blake and G. V. Ramsey, 1951, New York, Ronald Press Ltd, gives a most stimulating introduction to this work. These two books give comprehensive bibliographies. *Doubt and Certainty in Science*, by J. Z. Young, 1951, Oxford, Clarendon Press, gives a good basis for new thinking about science. 'Psychology and Scientific Research', by H. Cantril, A. Ames Jr, A. H. Hastorf, and W. H. Ittelson, in *Science* 110, 1949, is an extremely important and thought-provoking paper. 'Visual perception and the rotating trapezoidal window', *Psychological Monographs*, 65, pp. 32, 1951, by Adelbert Ames Jr, though on a narrow aspect of his work, should be read for an exquisite example of clear thinking and beautiful exposition. *Education for What is Real*, by E. C. Kelley, 1947, New York, Harper Bros, and *The Why of Man's Experience*, by H. Cantril, 1950, New York, Macmillan Co., illustrate the implications of new ways of thinking about perception for the more general problems of human behaviour.

FAMOUS ANIMALS – 6
THE DOGFISH

JOHN E. HARRIS

Photogravure illustrations between pp. 64 and 65

IT is curious to reflect that many of the animals used in teaching elementary zoology are from a strictly zoological point of view very atypical. The reason for this is clear; such types for dissection are selected largely on grounds which have little to do with their anatomy – but with their convenient size, cheapness, and availability. From the evolutionary point of view, these characteristics do have a selective value – since they are indicators of 'success' (if one may use the word) in size and number at least. Nevertheless, such 'successful' forms are likely to be specialized organisms.

The result of this situation has been the curious paradox that the main stream of advancement of knowledge in animal morphology has been developed by the study of less familiar forms and the common laboratory animals have been largely neglected as subjects for zoological research – at least until the great growth of animal physiology in the last forty years. This study of animal function demands experimental material which is readily available in considerable quantity and which survives well under laboratory conditions – precisely the qualities possessed by most of the animals used for elementary teaching. A whole flood of new information has thus been produced on the genetics of *Paramecium,* the locomotion of the earthworm, the egg case of the cockroach, and the blood circulation of the frog – to name only four examples.

To the generalizations above there is a striking exception in the dogfish. It is not only a common and convenient subject for laboratory work, but it does show a remarkable number of thoroughly representative features of its class. Consequently, fundamental researches on the dogfish have been carried out throughout the last 100 years and are still going on. The aim of this present article is to summarize a few of these historic contributions and then to concentrate rather on the more recent and less well-known studies which have not usually found their way into the elementary textbooks. In dealing with a highly complex animal such as a vertebrate it is necessary to assume that the reader has access to such a textbook, otherwise what follows would be too long and detailed for its purpose.

The dogfishes – there are two different species which are commonly used for study, the rough hound, *Scyliorhinus canicula,* and the spur-dog, *Squalus acanthias* (see Plates 10 and 11) – are small sharks and, with the skates and rays and a small group of specialized deep sea forms, form the great class of cartilaginous fishes contrasting with a second large class of bony fishes to which belong most of the common fresh water and marine fish of the present day. A tiny third class of bony fish includes the living lungfishes and that famous discovery of recent times, the coelacanth, important because they lie just off the line of descent which gave rise to all land-living animals including man himself.

We know little or nothing of the origin of these three classes of fish from still earlier fresh-water forms; species of all three existed side by side in Devonian seas, 300 million years ago. Within each class, however, the lines of evolutionary development are reasonably clear; that of the cartilaginous fish is shown in Fig. 1.

The feeding habits of sharks have changed a good deal in the course of their evolution. The modern dogfish is a carnivorous scavenger, preying on relatively slow-moving or moribund animals on the sea floor – chiefly other fishes. For this type of diet the bottom-living habit and keen olfactory sense is very well adapted. But the Devonian shark, *Cladoselache,* was obviously quite different in its habits. The enormous, forwardly placed eyes, widely gaping jaws, and powerful teeth all suggest that this early form was a very active and predatory type. The tail had a narrow root with lateral keels for streamlining its motion and

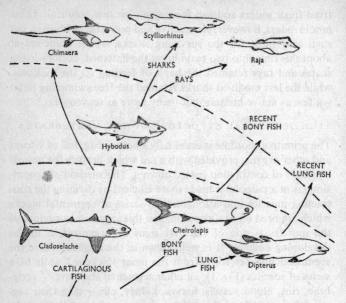

Fig. 1. The ancestry of the fishes. The broken lines indicate division
between Palaeozoic, Mesozoic, and recent geological eras.

its broad symmetrical scythe-like form indicates a high cruising
speed. The abundance of specimens as well as of different species
of *Cladoselache* testify to the ample scope then available for
these active hunters.

The sharks, however, passed through a relatively lean time in
Permian and Triassic periods, 200 million years ago. At that time
the bony fish which had earlier formed their prey (chiefly marine
'lungfishes') seem to have been in short supply; most of the true
bony fish were fresh-water forms at this time, and the successful
sharks developed pebble-like crushing teeth and ventrally placed
mouths suited for feeding on molluscs and similar bottom-living
forms. The Hybodonts with teeth and jaws of this type were the
main marine fishes of this period. But 120 million years ago, in
Cretaceous times, a new host of bony fishes invaded the sea

from fresh waters and fish food again became plentiful. These new invaders, however, were active and powerful swimmers, not such easy meat for the surviving sharks, which branched at about this time into two main lines; the flattened, bottom-living skates and rays retained the habit of feeding on the molluscs, while the less modified sharks retained the free swimming habit – a few as active hunters, but many more as scavengers.

THE SEGMENTAL STRUCTURE OF THE VERTEBRATES

The primitive chordate is essentially a hollow bag, full of viscera and other organs, provided with a tail which propels the animal by waves of contraction passed down it. This method of propulsion (as in a tadpole) is made more efficient by dividing the contracting muscles into a longitudinal series of segmental blocks which are fired off in succession, and this segmental structure of the muscles is one of the first signs of organization in the developing embryo. It is well shown in the dogfish, where the segmental muscles form from the inner thickened walls of a series of somites (Fig. 1); all other segmental structures – vertebrae, ribs, blood vessels, nerves, kidney, etc. – take their segmental pattern from this primary segmentation of the muscle. If one somite is cut out in the early embryo, all the corresponding segmental organs fail to develop.

This picture is quite comprehensible when applied to the *body* of a vertebrate like the fish, but what of the head? Its main muscles are those of the jaws, hyoid and gill arches, with six tiny strips serving to rotate the eyeball; its skeleton is an elaborate skull quite unlike a vertebral column; its nervous system a complex brain with a bewildering tangle of nerves running out in all directions.

F. M. Balfour, a brilliant young Cambridge zoologist, who died in a mountaineering accident at the age of only 31, first provided the key to this puzzle; he found in the head of the embryo dogfish a series of eight somites forming a complete sequence with those of the body (Balfour, 1874–8). Following him, Marshall (1881–2) and van Wijhe (1882) discovered that the six eye muscles were formed from three of these head somites

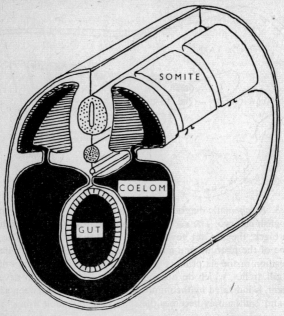

Fig. 2. A dissected diagram to show the segmental structure
of the vertebrate body.

and represented the adult segmental head muscles; those of the
next two segments atrophy during the growth of the auditory
capsule which obliterates them; the remaining three segmental
muscles are recognizable as such in the adult. The muscles of the
jaw, hyoid, and gill arches are of a different origin; though they
are histologically like the swimming muscles, they are derived
from the smooth muscle producing the contractions of the gut
and are not developed from the somites. It is generally believed
that the jaws and gill arches correspond in position to head segments only because the holes (spiracle and gill openings) between each of these arches originally broke through to the
exterior at the natural weak points between the somites (see
Fig. 3 and Plate 12).

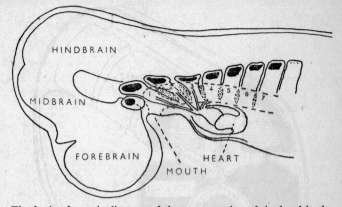

Fig. 3. A schematic diagram of the segmentation of the head in the dogfish embryo. The eight cavities of the head somites are shown in black; they do not however develop at the same time. The outline of the pharynx and gut is shown in dashes, together with the position of the six primary gill slits (stippled). The position of the 7 gill arches, which do not appear until a later stage in development, is indicated by the numbers 1–7. The gill slit between arches 1 and 2 ultimately becomes the spiracle of the adult fish.

Space does not permit the detailed story of the remaining head structures to be told here; it can be found in the very full account by Goodrich (1930). It is sufficient to add that, corresponding to these head somites, the hind brain with its nerves and the posterior part of the skull develop in a recognizably segmental manner; the nose and eye, however, together with their nerves and corresponding regions of the brain lie in front of this segmented portion. We get a vivid picture in the evolution of the early vertebrates of the continued invasion of a primitively segmental body by an ever-increasing mass of complex sensory, feeding and breathing apparatus – blurred snapshots in the long evolutionary time scale recognizable in the smooth sequence of the motion picture of embryonic development.

It would, however, be unfair to the dogfish to omit one other classical example of its contribution to the story of vertebrate segmentation. In the early bony fishes which swarmed in Devonian seas the characteristic pectoral and pelvic fin had a long central skeletal axis from which lateral cartilages projected like the barbs from a feather. (The now famous coelacanth fish possesses fins of a similar type.) Side by side with these fishes swam *Cladoselache*, a shark with a broad-based horizontal flap-like fin, its axis like a long hinge embedded in the body surface, with a series of radial struts projecting out from it to support the triangular fin flap. Which was the more primitive fin form, and how did these fins arise – since the earlier 'fishes' did not possess them? Gegenbauer (1878) thought the feather-like fin was the original one and derived it and its pectoral girdle from a gill arch; Balfour, on the other hand, thought the shark type was more primitive, originating from a lateral flap of skin moved by segmental body muscles and supported by segmental cartilages; faint echoes of this seventy-year-old controversy still persist to the present day. The weight of evidence in favour of Balfour's theory was overwhelmingly supported by the studies of Goodrich (1906), who showed that the muscles and nerves of the embryonic dogfish pectoral and pelvic fins were budded off from the segmental body musculature; even in man, the nerves to the muscles of the arm show a faintly recognizable segmental sequence.

SKELETON

The skeleton of the dogfish presents many points of interest. Apart from the placoid scales and teeth it is entirely composed of cartilage – a characteristic which is diagnostic of the great group Chondrichthyes to which it belongs. Many of the fossil sharks showed heavy calcification of this cartilage, but true bone structure is never found even in this highly mineralized skeleton. Yet among still more primitive vertebrates the fossil forms we know are nearly all armoured by a true bony plating. This dermal armour of bone has a histological structure which suggests the fusion of an enormous number of small surface scales with an underlying bony plate; beneath it was often a typical endoskeleton of calcified cartilage. The growth of such a suit of armour must have been an awkward problem, as it often formed almost a complete unbroken carapace over the head and thoracic region. It has been suggested that perhaps it did *not* grow in some forms (in which all the fossil specimens found appear to be full grown); growth would be first completed in an unarmoured condition and the plating would be consolidated only when the full size had been attained. If so, and if the cartilaginous fishes arose from a stock of this type, they could be looked upon as its *neotenous* descendants – i.e. like the modern axolotl, reproducing in a persistent 'larval' stage. Only the placoid scales would remain as protective remnants of this once abundant dermal bone. Cartilage, on the other hand, being a matrix continuously secreted by cells embedded in it, can grow at any point within its volume – it is, as Romer (1949) has said, an *embryonic tissue*. An internal skeleton of cartilage easily provides for indefinite growth of the body, and it is strong enough to form a perfectly practicable skeleton even in the 50-ft whaleshark, the largest fish existing today.

Many of the early sharks possessed teeth so like their scales that it is evident that placoid scales and teeth have a common origin. Both are shed and replaced as required, both are formed from a bony substance – dentine – surrounding a vascular pulp cavity, and both have a hard 'enamel' layer on the surface. This enamel is, however, not identical with that found in the teeth of mammals, for it is formed in mesodermal dentine by infiltration of hydroxyapatite into the surface of the dentine itself – not by ectodermal secretion of a separate surface layer (Kvam, 1950).

BLOOD CIRCULATION AND EXCRETORY SYSTEM

The blood system of the dogfish is too familiar a subject for dissection to merit a detailed description, but there are one or two features of interest which are worth mentioning. Unlike the mammal, with its 'double', figure-of-8 circulation where blood flows through the heart twice during each complete passage round the body: heart→lungs→heart→body, the dogfish has a single circulation. Blood passes from the ventricle of the heart, through the gill capillaries where it is oxygenated, to the arteries and capillaries of the body; it returns to the heart by a system of thin-walled very large veins or sinuses. The blood pressure on emerging from the heart is 30 mm. of mercury, as compared with 75 mm. in the salmon and 120 mm. in mammals; in the arteries to the dogfish body it is less than 10 mm.; the 20 mm. difference is accounted for by frictional losses in the gill capillaries. Obviously, by the time the blood has passed through the capillaries of the body tissues as well, it will have very little residual pressure; indeed it seems likely that there is no excess pressure in the venous sinuses, which are in fact too large and thin-walled to maintain one. The difficulty of filling the heart under such conditions is solved by enclosing the heart in what is for all practical purposes a firm box of connective tissue and cartilage, based on the pectoral girdle, and lined by the pericardium. When the vigorous contraction of the auricle and ventricle take place, the pressure in this pericardial cavity actually falls below zero, according to Skramlik (1935); the thin-walled entrance chamber of the heart, the sinus venosus, is thus partly filled under reduced pressure, exactly as in the filling of the lungs of a mammal with air.

In estimating the efficiency of the blood circulation, a great many factors have to be taken into account, some of which we do not know for the dogfish – or for any of its relatives. But the following account summarizes the general picture. The oxygen consumption per gram is low – only one quarter of that of the trout or frog and one twelfth of that of the rabbit (though this last is measured at the high mammalian body temperature). The blood volume is surprisingly high – 3.7 per cent of body volume – about twice as high as that of the bony fish; if, however, one can judge from the skate, the oxygen-carrying capacity of the blood is only about half that of the bony fish, so that the total available oxygen would be about the same. The efficiency of the gills is low; about 46 per cent of the oxygen content is removed from the respiratory water current, as opposed to 80 per cent in the trout. This is clearly connected with the short gill filaments in the dogfish; those of the bony fishes are very greatly elongated in comparison; though in all fishes the ingenious device is adopted of having the blood in the gills flow in the opposite direction to that of the water. The stream of well-oxygenated water just entering the gills (from the pharynx) thus meets the most highly oxygenated blood, while poorly oxygenated blood is in contact with water from which some oxygen has already been extracted.

The high total oxygen content of the blood in relation to the requirements of the dogfish explains why it is so tenacious of life when hooked and brought in – in contrast to the more active mackerel and trout. It suggests that the whole respiratory system is working in a fairly leisurely fashion – a relatively small volume of water passing over the small gill surface, and a low blood pressure producing a much less active circulation, nevertheless ample for the requirements of the fish.

The kidneys of the dogfish have been the subject of a number of interesting studies both morphological and physiological. It was in the classical work of Balfour (1881) that the idea was first put forward that the vertebrate kidney developed as a segmental series of funnels opening into the coelom, and discharging to the exterior by a common longitudinal duct. Later work by Borcea (1905) on the spiny dogfish and by Goodrich (1930) on *Scyliorhinus* showed that Balfour's story was oversimplified, and that in many respects the development of the dogfish kidney is unusual, but the significance of Balfour's discovery remains unchanged.

If the dogfish kidney has stimulated many important morphological investigations, its physiology has shown equally fascinating possibilities. The story has been told in detail by H. W. Smith (1936). The blood of the dogfish contains over 2 per cent of urea – a typical excretory product of many higher vertebrates. The enzyme, arginase, responsible for its production is present in large amounts in all the body tissues except blood and brain; urea does not escape through the gills, and the kidney possesses a special mechanism for pumping it back into the blood almost as fast as it leaks out through the glomerular filter.

These characteristics have been found in all the sharks and

rays that have been examined, and it is clear that the evolutionary origin of this habit is very old. The probability is that it
developed when the ancestors of the sharks migrated from fresh
water into the sea. This meant that the osmotic pressure of the
blood was much less than that of the new surrounding medium –
the sea water. The tendency for the blood to lose water osmotic-
ally to the sea water was opposed by retaining sufficient urea in
the blood to counteract the osmotic effect of the extra salts in
the sea water; the balance has been struck at the point where
there is, in fact, a slight *inflow* of water from the environment,
which can be dealt with by the kidney. The tissues of the body
are more than merely tolerant of this urea; they have evidently
become so habituated to it that the heart will not beat in a
physiological solution which does not contain urea, and the egg
case is provided with a store of urea when it is laid.

This ingenious development may well have occurred on other
occasions in the evolution of fishes, though it is not found in
modern bony fish, which deal with the same problem by drinking sea water and excreting chloride through the gills. Blood
urea is, however, present in the living fresh-water lungfish,
where it is brought into action during the dry season when the
fish aestivates in a mud cocoon. (Since the essential feature of
the problem which the animal has to solve is loss of water to the
environment, life in the sea and life on the land under conditions
where drinking fresh water is impossible are similar in this
respect.) These lungfish are related, though distantly, to the
newly discovered living marine coelacanths *Latimeria* and
Malania; we may therefore guess that when one of these is
finally brought back alive, it will be found also to use urea as an
osmotic buffer.

LOCOMOTION AND SENSE ORGANS

A large amount of very interesting work has been done on the
swimming of the dogfish. In the embryo dogfish, 3 millimetres
in length and possessing only 15 somites, rhythmical contraction
of the body muscles produces a side to side bending of the head.
This does not produce any forward movement of the embryo

(which at this stage is attached over half the length of its body to the yolk sac), but it may help to oxygenate it and to keep the albumen in motion. Wintrebert in 1920 discovered that this rhythmical muscular contraction was quite independent of nerve control, and that it continued when the nervous system was completely removed. For several days the embryonic 'voluntary' muscle behaves like the automatically contracting heart muscle of all vertebrates, until finally the nervous system attains complete control over the rhythm, which then stops if the nerve cord is excised.

Even in the adult a high degree of local automaticity persists in the true swimming movements. Gray and Sand (1936) showed that rhythmical swimming movements persisted when the whole brain was severed from the spinal cord; characteristic reflex responses can be obtained from such a spinal fish. This work stimulated interest in an important physiological controversy – whether rhythmical patterns of movement, as in walking or swimming, are produced by rhythmical sensory stimulation, or whether they are inherent in the central nervous system and are merely controlled by such stimuli. Lissman (1946) succeeded in cutting the whole of the sensory nerve roots in a spinal dogfish and found that rhythmical swimming no longer occurred; some sensory input to the nerve cord is therefore essential, though it may only serve to raise the general level of excitation in the cord – the rhythm may still be of central origin. (See Plate 13.)

Following on the very interesting early studies by Marey (1893), Gray (1933) has shown that in the dogfish, as in many other fishes, swimming is accomplished by waves of alternate contractions passing down the body from head to tail; these throw the body into a series of undulations which propel the water backwards in a manner similar to the action of a screw propeller – by the reaction of an inclined plane moving through the liquid. Turning, however, is accomplished, not by using the tail as a rudder, but by flexing the body so that the head takes up the new direction first. The fish, in fact, steers like a car and not a boat.

The dogfish, having no swim bladder, is heavier than water; its specific gravity is 1.06, that of sea-water is 1.03, consequently it sinks if it is at rest and, while in movement, lift forces must be developed to keep it up. Ahlborn (1896) suggested that the pectoral fins and lower lobe of the tail served this purpose, and Grove and Newell (1936) confirmed the mechanical action of such a ventral tail flap.* The writer (Harris, 1936) made a plaster model of the American smooth dogfish, *Mustelus canis,* and 'flew' it in a wind tunnel to investigate the forces on the other fins. The pectoral fins could readily be tilted to produce the desired lift, and other interesting features also came to light. The large pectoral fins make the steering, rising and diving unstable, but capable of very delicate and accurate control; their elaborate musculature and reflex mechanisms are readily explicable on this basis. (The article by J. Maynard Smith on 'Birds as Aeroplanes' in *New Biology 14* also mentions this problem.) The small pelvic fins had very little effect on the model dogfish, though being well behind the centre of gravity they must assist horizontal stability to some extent – particularly when the tail is not producing a lift force.

Incidentally, no shark appears to possess the power of swimming backwards. All bony fish can do so with the help of their very mobile fins, and the lamprey and eel can wriggle backwards by passing waves of muscular contraction forward from the tail to the head. This backward-swimming mechanism appears to depend on the use of giant fibres in the spinal cord which transmit impulses directly from the motor centres of the brain to the hind end of the body; such centres and fibres (the Müller fibres of the lamprey) are absent in sharks, which always retreat by turning round and swimming away.

Any free swimming predatory organism like the dogfish must naturally possess an elaborate sensory apparatus for guiding and controlling its movements. All three 'primary' sense organs, eye, ear, and nose, are well developed in *Scylliorhinus.* As is well

*All the different groups of bony fishes evolved an air bladder (or lung) sometime during their history; it is interesting to note therefore that, starting with a tail similar to that of the dogfish, all bony fish have later developed a mechanically symmetrical tail fin.

known, the olfactory sense is very highly developed in all carti-laginous fishes and their fore-brain is largely a relay-station for olfactory impulses – not a structure dealing with learned be-haviour. Removal of the whole fore-brain has therefore surpris-ingly little effect on the behaviour.

The eye presents a number of interesting features best re-viewed in the work of Walls (1942). It is, like the human eye, normally focussed for distant objects, and it has to be accom-modated for near vision. But this accommodation is brought about by moving the lens away from the retina and not by changing its shape. The retina itself is largely, if not entirely, composed of rods – which means that the fish is adapted for life in relatively low light intensities and is colour blind; the so-called visual purple of the rods has its maximum sensitivity to light at 505 mμ wavelength. While this is also close to the wave-length for the maximum penetration of light into coastal sea water this is true of most visual purples – and merely means that this light-sensitive pigment was evolved for use in water – to that extent we all bear evidence of our aquatic ancestry.

Another adaptation to vision in dim light is provided by the presence of a silvery layer or *tapetum* below the light-sensitive cells of the retina; the *tapetum* reflects extra light on to the cells. In some dogfishes this layer takes the form of a series of inclined planes which can be shuttered in strong light by a black pigment layer of contractile cells. In strong light the iris also closes to an oblique slit.

There is little doubt that in its normal habitat sight plays as important a part as smell. An elaborate 'ear' system is present and, in view of the ease with which delicate dissections can be made on a cartilaginous skull, many important researches have been initiated on this organ. Most of the ear in fishes is not a hearing organ but is concerned with stabilizing the eye move-ments when the body of the fish rolls and turns, thus keeping the visual field constant. Independent voluntary eye movements do not occur. True hearing is probably present, though limited to a small patch of sensory hairs in the utriculus. The main centre for receptions of low frequency vibrations is the lateral line system which according to Pumphrey (1951) is an extremely sensitive and accurate method of locating objects such as other fish in the neighbourhood.

Pumphrey points out that a group of vibration receptors – in this case cells possessing hairs carrying at their tips a concretion of heavy material – will respond to a distant vibration according to their distance from the source of 'sound'. If, therefore, they are spread over a considerable length of body, and at the same time their intensity of stimulation can be compared by feeding the nervous impulses into a common centre, the apparatus will function rather like a radio direction-finding aerial. This feature – wide 'spread' of the sense organs with a single centre for analysis – is precisely that possessed by the lateral line system which, though it extends over the whole body, is innervated by cranial nerves from a single centre in the medulla.

REPRODUCTION AND DEVELOPMENT

All the cartilaginous fish produce large yolky eggs, generally protected by a horny egg case, and internal fertilization is therefore a necessity. In a few forms, including the spiny dogfish, the whole development takes place in the oviduct of the mother, a number of eggs sharing a common thin-walled egg-capsule. Occasionally there is a 'placental' attachment of the yolk sac to the uterine wall, a fact which was known to Aristotle.

In view of this internal fertilization, it is interesting to find that

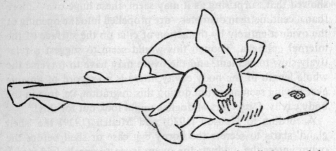

Fig. 4. Mating in the common dogfish; the male is coiled around the body of the female (after Bolau).

claspers on the pelvic fins of the male which pass the sperm into the cloaca of the female do not occur before the Hybodont sharks (except in the recently described Devonian form *Diademodus,* Harris (1951)). Pairing in the common dogfish has been described by Bolau (1881); the male coils itself around the body of the female in a curious back-to-back position (see Fig. 4). This method will provide a firm grip in a rough-skinned form like *Scyliorhinus,* but in smoother-skinned sharks or those with less flexible bodies it can scarcely be practicable. In the Hybodonts there is a hook-shaped spine on the side of the head in the male which would help to anchor it to the female during pairing; some specimens of *Cladoselache* have a large head spine which may have functioned in the same way. The modern Chimaeroid fishes have a spiny head clasper in the male which Dean (1906) showed was responsible for producing a pattern of marks at the base of the dorsal fin of the female. It therefore looks as though this peculiar pairing behaviour is of great antiquity, and this may explain the persistence of dorsal fin spines in so many different species. (See Plate 2.)

Mature females of the common rough hound lay eggs through some ten months of the year; some authors say all the year round. Though there is only one ovary, it appears that two eggs are released more or less simultaneously, one passing to each oviduct; the author (Harris, 1951) has estimated that each female must lay at least 10 eggs per month. Metten (1939) showed that, surprising as it may seem, these huge ova – more than a centimetre in diameter – are propelled into the opening of the oviduct entirely by the action of cilia on the surface of the internal epithelia. Though this would seem to suggest a relatively slow movement, and the ovum may have to traverse the whole length of the body cavity, there is no record of anyone ever having seen an ovum during this migration, i.e. free in the body cavity. Dissectors of dogfish might look out for this!

According to Hobson (1930) and Metten (1939) the 'shell gland' starts to secrete the horny egg case or shell before the ovum enters the oviduct; the ovum is, so to speak, laid into a partially completed case, which is then closed over by the secretion of the remaining portion. Before this occurs the egg is fertilized by sperm stored in the folds of the wall of the shell gland, which also acts as a sperm reservoir; pairing probably occurs rather rarely. An isolated female ray has been known to lay 30 fertile eggs in succession (Clark, 1922) and it is reasonable to suppose that this also applies to the dogfish.

The fertilized eggs develop very slowly; a 48-day-old dogfish embryo is at almost the same stage as a 48-hour chick embryo. This difference is in fact explained by the different temperature of development. That of the dogfish is taken from experiments at 11.5° C.; its rate of development increases 1.6 times for each 4° C. rise in temperature. Consequently, if it could survive at the incubation temperature of the chick, the dogfish would reach a particular stage in about 1/24th of the time – exactly the same as the chick. The exact agreement is of course fortuitous; nevertheless it does emphasize the fact that both dogfish and hen lay eggs with a large amount of yolk, slowing down the rate of development to a similar extent – the less heavily yolked egg of the frog develops about three times as rapidly. (The yolk-less egg of the mammal, however, develops very slowly, but under quite different conditions.) Six months to a year after it is laid, the dogfish egg hatches to produce a young fish which is a miniature of the adult.

The later life history of the dogfish has not been worked out in detail. Dr G. A. Steven of the Marine Biological Station at Plymouth tells me that 'fingerling' (i.e. very young, recently hatched) dogfish are never caught by the laboratory research vessels; it would be interesting to know where they spend the first year or so of their life. No method has yet been worked out for estimating the age of a dogfish, and most of the dogfish caught for laboratory purposes seem to be surprisingly uniform in size. Since these large fish are nearly all sexually mature specimens, it looks as though the early life may be spent off-shore, the mature fish returning to shallow water perhaps for the purpose of breeding or egg laying. There is a curious disproportion in the numbers of the two sexes, first reported by Ford (1921) to vary throughout the year. At Plymouth the males preponderate during the winter months, females in summer. The same difference was found in fish from the Bristol Channel (Harris, 1952), but in reverse; 80 per cent of the fish were females from September to February and there was a great increase of males in spring and early summer. This 'arrival' of males in the spring is not necessarily connected with the breeding season, as the proportion of females laying eggs reaches its maximum in January in the Bristol Channel, and thereafter declines slightly.

It is inevitable that an account such as this should be sketchy and omit much work that has been done on the dogfish – and even more that obviously remains to be done. Apart from an interesting account of the morphology of the adrenal complex, we know little of the endocrine system, especially of its function. The trigger mechanisms of the reproductive cycle, the take-over by the nervous system of the automatic muscle contractions in the embryo, the function of rectal glands and spiracle, the early life history in the sea and the meaning of the peculiar sex ratio in the adults – all still remain to be studied. There is an embryonic sensory nervous system which disappears before hatching; the idea of a special urea-absorbing segment in the kidney tubule has only this year been shown to be false; the mechanical 'reason' for the peculiar folded form of the fish myotome has never been satisfactorily explained. One could write a second article of equal length on what we do not know about the common dogfish. But if this article has stimulated a few interesting ideas, especially among those whose job is to teach and those whose fate it is to learn about the dogfish, it will have served its purpose.

FURTHER READING

Much of the work described in the account above has been taken from original scientific papers or reviews; it is not therefore easily accessible but, as authors' names and dates are given, a reference to the appropriate annual volume of Zoological Record will reveal the source of the information quoted. A good general account of the cartilaginous fishes is given in J. Z. Young, *Life of Vertebrates*, Oxford University Press.

FAMOUS PLANTS–4
CHLORELLA

G. E. FOGG

Photogravure illustration between pp. 64 and 65

THE plants which have been considered in previous articles in this series have become familiar to generations of students because they have been accepted as representative types particularly suitable for teaching purposes. *Chlorella* is scarcely heard of in the classroom, but has achieved fame as a result of its possession of qualities which make it of pre-eminent value in research. Although this organism is the object of highly specialized studies, it is also of considerable general interest as the best-known example of a class of micro-organisms which plays a fundamental part in the economy of nature and which may come to be of some direct importance to man.

The genus *Chlorella* includes a number of species of green plants, abundant in soil, fresh water and other habitats, the individuals of which each consist of a single cell of the order of 5 to 10 microns in diameter (a micron or μ is 0.001 mm. or about 0.00004 inch). Unicellular plants of this sort were just becoming known towards the end of the eighteenth century when Joseph Priestley, one of the discoverers of oxygen and a pioneer worker on photosynthesis, became interested in the 'green matter' which appeared by chance in the water in his apparatus. He observed that this green matter was particularly active in producing 'dephlogisticated air', i.e. oxygen, when illuminated, and he carried out many experiments which showed that it would grow under a wide range of conditions. In the second volume of his 'Experiments and observations relating to various branches of natural philosophy', published in 1781, he expressed the conviction that the green matter was of a plant-like nature and commented that it did not seem to have been properly noticed by botanists.

Priestley did not describe the forms which he studied in sufficient detail for recognition, but it seems probable that *Chlorella* was among the principal components of his green matter.

Many unicellular green plants were described during the nineteenth century, but the genus *Chlorella* was not established until 1890. In this year the great Dutch microbiologist Beijerinck reported the isolation, in artificial culture uncontaminated by other micro-organisms, of a species which he called *Chlorella vulgaris,* the method used being an adaptation of that which Koch had recently devised for obtaining pure cultures of bacteria. This consisted in dispersing a small amount of ditch water containing the organism in molten gelatine which was afterwards poured on to a plate and allowed to set. On exposure to suitable conditions, colonies of *Chlorella* developed within the gelatine and some of them were sufficiently well separated from colonies of other organisms to be picked out, inoculated into fresh medium, and grown as pure cultures. Beijerinck carried out a number of experiments with his cultures and showed, among other things, that *Chlorella,* although photosynthetic like other green plants, can also grow in the dark if provided with suitable organic substances. He observed that the organism reproduced only by simple division of its cells and that motile cells were never formed under any of the conditions of culture which he used. Many kinds of physiological investigation with green plants cannot be carried out unless the material is uncontaminated with other organisms such as bacteria and fungi. By showing how unicellular plants such as *Chlorella* could be obtained and handled in pure culture Beijerinck paved the way for important advances in plant physiology.

Further studies on *Chlorella* continued to be made, but the organism did not attract any particular attention until it was used by the biochemist Warburg in his studies on photosynthesis. Because of their complex structure flowering plants afford rather unfavourable material for the investigation of the mechanism of this process. For example, the apparently simple determination of the effect of carbon dioxide concentration on the rate of photosynthesis in a flowering plant yields results which become ambiguous when it is considered that the carbon dioxide in the external atmosphere must from thence diffuse via the stomata, intercellular air spaces, cell walls and protoplasm, so that it is extremely difficult to be sure of its actual concentration at the site of photosynthesis. Again, because the cells in which photosynthesis occurs are continually interchanging materials with cells of other kinds, both in the same leaf and in other parts of the plant, it is more difficult than it otherwise might be to find out the nature and amount of the products of photosynthesis. Another difficulty with flowering plants is that it is not easy to maintain a continuous supply of plant material of standard physiological properties under laboratory conditions. Realizing this, Warburg sought the help of his uncle, a botanist, in finding a more suitable organism. A species of *Chlorella* was selected and formed the experimental material for a series of fundamental researches on photosynthesis the first of which was published in 1919. The advantages of *Chlorella* for this work were many. Because it is unicellular and of minute size, diffusion of materials between the cells and the aqueous medium in which they are contained is extremely rapid and if the suspension is kept stirred so that the cells do not settle out one can be sure that the concentration of any given substance at their surface is the same as that supplied in the bulk of the medium. *Chlorella* will tolerate high concentrations of substances such as carbon dioxide and nutrient salts and will continue to function through a wide range of experimental conditions. Its cells are nearly uniform in size and properties, and cell division results in the production of more cells of the same sort. It grows rapidly and is easily maintained in a healthy condition in pure culture in a simple solution of mineral salts. If culture conditions are standardized, material of consistent behaviour can be obtained at any time of the year.

Since it was first used by Warburg, *Chlorella* has been used extensively in research on photosynthesis and a large part of our present knowledge of the mechanism of this process is based on results obtained with this and related organisms (see the article on the mechanism of photosynthesis in *New Biology 11*).

It is interesting that the green matter which so attracted Priestley should thus have come to play a fundamental role in the development of a field of knowledge which he was the first to enter. However, *Chlorella* has attributes other than a capacity for photosynthesis and these have also received attention, and at this point it seems best to abandon the historical approach for a consideration of the organism in a more systematic fashion.

The genus *Chlorella* is classified in the order Chlorococcales of the class Chlorophyceae. This class is that which includes green algae, such as *Chlamydomonas, Volvox, Spirogyra,* and *Oedogonium,* familiar to those who have done an elementary course in botany. In structure green algae range from simple forms such as *Chlorella* to elaborate filamentous types and comparatively large conspicuous species such as *Ulva,* the sea-lettuce, and *Chara,* the stone-wort. What appear to be the most primitive types are put in the order Volvocales. The principal difference between this and the Chlorococcales is that its members normally possess flagella and are motile, whereas members of the Chlorococcales are normally non-motile, flagellated cells, if they are formed at all, being confined to the reproductive phases of the life-cycle. *Chlamydomonas* (see *New Biology 6*), a member of the Volvocales, is a unicellular plant which normally has flagella but which under certain circumstances is non-motile and is then very similar to *Chlorella.* In *Chlorella* the tendency seen in *Chlamydomonas* has become a permanent feature and motile cells are absent even during reproduction. This characteristic is the one accepted as separating the genus from forms such as *Chlorococcum,* otherwise very similar, which produce motile cells during reproduction. However, it may be doubted whether the loss of motile stages in *Chlorella* is absolute. Thus an organism which has been maintained in culture for nearly thirty years as *Chlorella vulgaris* appears very occasionally to produce flagellated cells. It does not seem unlikely that there should be a continuous series of forms between those that normally produce motile stages and those that never do, and the separation of *Chlorella* from related genera may thus be artificial. Certain species in the Volvocales are multicellular, e.g. *Volvox* (see *New Biology 6*), and this development has its parallel in the Chlorococcales, which includes various multicellular organisms the individual cells of which are essentially like *Chlorella*.

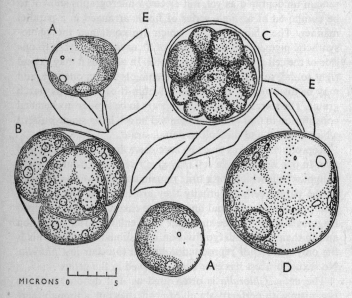

Fig. 1. *Chlorella vulgaris*; A, cells from young culture, their chloroplasts are shaded; B, dividing cell; C, cell from old culture, containing large amounts of starch; D, vacuolated cell from old culture, the large conspicuous body in the chloroplast is the pyrenoid; E, cell wall fragments.

The cell structure of *Chlorella vulgaris* appears to be simple (Fig. 1), but because of the small size of the organism has not been studied very closely. The cell wall, which is thin, has an inner layer which becomes violet on treatment with strong sulphuric acid and iodine, a reaction generally assumed to indicate the presence of cellulose. However, this test is not very reliable and there are reasons for supposing that cellulose is not, in fact, present. While cellulose is the characteristic component of the cell wall in higher plants, it is not invariably present in green algae and is altogether lacking in certain other algal groups, e.g. the diatoms. The chemical components of the wall of *Chlorella* remain unidentified as yet, but electron micrographs show it to be composed of a single series of fibrils arranged in a parallel manner. The chloroplast, in which are contained the photosynthetic pigments, is in the form of a curved plate lying to one side of the cell and against the cell wall. In old cells it may extend right round, so that only a small opening is left on one side, and may be distorted by the presence within it of numerous starch grains. The starch of *Chlorella* appears to be similar in chemical constitution to that of higher plants. The cell has a single nucleus which is small and difficult to demonstrate.

Reproduction takes place by successive divisions of a cell into two. In this way a single cell may give rise to two, four, or eight daughter cells which for a time remain enclosed within the wall of the parent cell. Eventually they are liberated, the old wall splitting along meridional lines to give characteristically shaped fragments (Fig. 1). The daughter cells enlarge after liberation and in their turn undergo division in a similar manner. This is the only method of reproduction known to occur in *Chlorella*. No sexual process has ever been observed in the genus.

The name *Chlorella* is often used as if it denoted a single organism with perfectly standard properties but, although there would at first sight appear to be little scope for variation, this is far from being so. Some nine or more species have been distinguished by details of cell structure and by physiological characteristics. Besides *C. vulgaris* it is worth mentioning *C. pyrenoidosa,* much used in research and characterized by the possession of a conspicuous *pyrenoid* (a body in the chloroplast which seems especially concerned in starch formation); *C. variegata* which has a marked tendency to lose its photosynthetic pigments; and *C. conductrix,* similar in appearance to *C. vulgaris* but forming symbiotic associations with animals. *C. conductrix* is found within the cells of *Hydra, Stentor,* and *Paramecium,* for example, to which it evidently supplies carbohydrates in exchange for nitrogenous materials. Apart from differences which are considered to be sufficiently important to warrant this differentiation into species, there is considerable variation to be found in *Chlorella*. Nearly every strain which has been isolated has its own distinctive characteristics, and strains which seem identical in appearance may show consistent differences in physiological properties such as growth rate and reaction to poisons.

Species of *Chlorella* are to be found in a wide variety of habitats. They are common in soils and may be abundant on the surface if this is damp. Although living cells are to be found at depths of many centimetres below the surface and although it has been demonstrated that they are capable of growing under such circumstances, it does not appear that *Chlorella* is of anything like the same importance in such situations as are fungi and bacteria. Species of *Chlorella* are abundant in small ponds and pools especially when these are contaminated with organic matter. Their capacity to supplement photosynthesis by assimilation of organic substances, to be discussed later, is evidently of biological value here. *Chlorella* is not characteristic of the open waters of lakes or the seas, but its species are to be found in the littoral regions of such bodies of water. *Chlorella* is often a constituent of the green powdery growth to be found on tree trunks and damp walls. It is extremely resistant to desiccation – cells have been found to revive after a year in the dry condition – and this contributes to its survival in such situations. Growth, however, is restricted to periods of dampness. As Priestley surmised, desiccated cells of *Chlorella* and similar algae will be dispersed by the wind and will develop in any suitable situation that they reach. Because of this and its tolerance of physiologically extreme concentrations of various substances *Chlorella* is a familiar contaminant of laboratory reagents.

In considering the nutrition of *Chlorella* attention must be given first to its requirement for inorganic salts. Besides carbon, hydrogen, and oxygen, it is necessary to supply nitrogen, sulphur, phosphorus, potassium, and magnesium, in relatively large amounts if growth is to take place. These elements must be supplied in suitable form. Sulphur, for example, is assimilated as sulphate, but not as the element or as sulphite. Nitrogen càn be assimilated as ammonia, nitrate or in certain organic forms, but not, apparently, as the element. These requirements are similar to those of higher plants with the exception that these require calcium in substantial amounts whereas *Chlorella,* although it may possibly require this element in extremely minute traces, can grow in its apparent absence. In addition to the major mineral nutrients *Chlorella* needs minute traces of other elements. Of these iron and manganese are needed in greatest amounts, whereas zinc and copper have been shown to be necessary in amounts of the order of only a hundredth of a part per million parts of culture solution. The same elements at even slightly higher concentrations prove toxic to *Chlorella.* Thus there is often enough copper ion in ordinary distilled water to inhibit totally the growth of this alga. As an example of a suitable solution for the culture of *Chlorella* the following may be given: ammonium nitrate, 0.5 g.; dipotassium hydrogen phosphate, 0.2 g.; magnesium sulphate ($MgSO_4.7H_2O$), 0.2 g.; calcium chloride, 0.1 g.; iron, as ferric chloride, 0.4 mg.; manganese, as manganese sulphate, 0.1 mg.; copper, as copper sulphate, 0.01 mg.; zinc, as zinc sulphate, 0.01 mg.; glass-distilled water, 1,000 ml. Possibly traces of elements other than those which have been mentioned are essential for the growth of *Chlorella* but, normally, sufficient of these will be present as impurity in the other salts used.

If cells of *Chlorella* are introduced into such a mineral solution which is then exposed to light and air and kept at a temperature of round about 20° C., the amount of organic matter in the culture will increase as a result of photosynthesis. The carbon dioxide, from which this organic matter is synthesized by means of energy obtained from the light, may be obtained by diffusion from the external air but, other conditions being optimal, greater rates of photosynthesis are achieved if the supply of this substance is increased, for example by bubbling carbon dioxide enriched air through the culture. A photosynthetic organism is not necessarily able to manufacture for itself all the complex organic substances that go to make up its protoplasm. Certain green algae related to *Chlorella,* for example, need to be supplied with traces of particular organic substances, notably vitamin B_1, if they are to grow, even though the major part of their organic matter is photosynthesized from carbon dioxide. The species of *Chlorella* usually met with, however, are completely self-sufficient in this respect and need no organic materials other than those which they can make for themselves from the primary products of photosynthesis.

Although it can thus maintain itself by photosynthesis, *Chlorella* can also make use of many kinds of preformed organic substances. For example, it will grow well in the dark if supplied with glucose. Here the glucose supplies both the carbon and the energy necessary for the synthesis of cell materials. Many substances besides glucose will support growth in the dark to a greater or lesser extent. These include other sugars, organic acids, and various protein preparations. The ease with which different organic substances are utilized may vary markedly according to the strain of *Chlorella* being examined. When conditions are optimal for photosynthesis the addition of organic carbon sources does not increase the rate of growth. However, if photosynthesis is limited, for example because of low light intensity, then such addition does increase growth, but only up to the rate which would be reached under otherwise similar conditions with maximum photosynthesis.

The species of *Chlorella* usually used in experimental work may be cultured indefinitely in the dark without losing their capacity for photosynthesis. Even after growth for many years with glucose as their only source of carbon such species remain bright green, having chlorophyll and other photosynthetic pigments just as they would do if grown in the light, and they can begin photosynthesis immediately when illuminated. This is in contrast to the state of affairs in higher plants, the majority of which cannot produce chlorophyll in the dark. *Chlorella variegata*, however, if grown in the dark turns yellow and only slowly becomes photosynthetic again on return to the light. Some cells may become white and in them the capacity for producing chlorophyll and carrying out photosynthesis is irrevocably lost.

This spontaneous loss of the capacity to produce photosynthetic pigments has the appearance of being a mutation. Apart from this the condition may be produced in other species of *Chlorella* by irradiation with X-rays. These colourless forms, which are, of course, entirely dependent upon preformed organic substances for their growth, but which are otherwise identical in form and metabolism with the green organisms from which they are derived, are very similar to colourless organisms of the genus *Prototheca* sometimes to be found in exudates from trees and in other situations rich in organic matter. *Prototheca* was first included among the fungi, but there can be little doubt that its species are *Chlorellas* which have lost their pigments under natural conditions in some manner similar to that studied in the laboratory. Specialization in nutrition can also occur in the other direction. A strain of *Chlorella* has been described which appears unable to grow except when photosynthesizing and which cannot grow in the dark even when supplied with apparently suitable organic substances.

When cells of *Chlorella* are placed under conditions suitable for growth they will continue to divide at regular intervals as long as the conditions remain the same. The interval between one division and the next is known as the *generation time* and its mean value is equal to the time taken for the total number of cells in a sample of a given size to double itself. Under the most favourable circumstances the mean generation time of *Chlorella* is about 15 hours. Since the population doubles at the end of each mean generation time the numbers would increase stepwise in geometrical progression were it not for the fact that divisions in different cells are nearly always out of phase so that the increase with any fairly large number of cells appears continuous. Such growth gives a curve of ever-increasing slope if a graph of cell numbers is plotted against time. This *exponential* type of curve can be transformed into a straight line if the logarithms of cell numbers are plotted instead of the numbers themselves. If cell counts are made on young cultures of *Chlorella* growing under suitable conditions and are plotted in this manner, the points are found to lie very closely along a straight line for several days.

The slope of this line is a measure of the efficiency with which the *Chlorella* reproduces itself, being greater the shorter the mean generation time.

Some readers may like to have these relationships expressed in mathematical symbols. For 'exponential' growth

$$n = n_o e^{rt}$$

where n and n_o are the cell numbers per unit volume of medium at the end and beginning respectively of the growth period t (usually taken in days), e is the base of natural logarithms and r the relative growth constant indicative of the efficiency of growth. Taking logarithms and rearranging, this expression becomes

$$r = \frac{\log_e n - \log_e n_o}{t}$$

and the mean generation time, g, is then given by

$$g = \frac{\log_e 2}{r} = \frac{0.693}{r}$$

in the same units as those in which t is expressed.

During the exponential phase of growth cell numbers build up very rapidly and it will be clear that this phase cannot normally continue for long either under natural conditions or in laboratory culture. Exponential growth can only be maintained indefinitely if fresh medium is added to an actively growing culture at a rate sufficient to keep the number of cells per unit volume constant. This method of culture, which is valuable for certain types of experimental work, produces *Chlorella* of very uniform physiological properties but requires rather complicated apparatus (see Plate 9). In cultures of the ordinary sort various factors may operate to bring exponential growth to a close. Most usually some nutrient material becomes in short supply or the cell population becomes so dense as to prevent light reaching the bulk of the culture with the result that photosynthesis becomes the limiting factor. Sometimes waste products of metabolism accumulating in the medium reach a concentration high enough to poison the cells.

Whatever the cause, growth sooner or later falls off and the number of cells becomes stationary. Cells which have thus stopped dividing are not necessarily in a condition to begin dividing immediately if introduced into fresh culture medium and there may then be a period of readjustment, the so-called 'lag phase', before exponential growth begins again. The whole sequence of events in the growth cycle is represented in Fig. 2.

During this growth cycle the cells of *Chlorella* do not remain unchanged in form, but rather show considerable variation. During the first few days of exponential growth average cell diameter decreases and the form of cell typical of this phase is one which is small, with dense protoplasmic contents, vacuoles poorly developed, small chloroplast and thin cell wall (Fig. 1, A). After the exponential phase is over the cells enlarge, the protoplasm becomes vacuolated, the chloroplast becomes relatively larger and may contain conspicuous amounts of starch, and the cell wall becomes thicker (Fig. 1, C and D). The increase in thickness of the cell wall may possibly account for the fact that, whereas in actively growing cultures the two-celled stage in division is most conspicuous, in older cultures the daughter cells remain together during as many as three consecutive divisions so that eight cells are frequently found held together by the wall of the parent cell.

These changes are visible manifestations of changes in the metabolism of the cells. During active growth the whole synthetic activity is directed towards formation of fresh protoplasm and the minimum amount of material is diverted for the production of storage and cell wall material not directly concerned in growth. Analyses of *Chlorella* at this stage show that as much as 60 per cent of the organic matter of the cell is protein, whereas carbohydrates and fats, both principally structural and reserve materials, make up 35 and 5 per cent respectively of the dry weight. Although the chloroplast is relatively small the efficiency with which light energy is utilized in photosynthesis is at its greatest at this stage. When growth is reduced and the culture passes into the post-exponential phases photosynthetic capacity declines also, but not necessarily to the same extent. It is perfectly

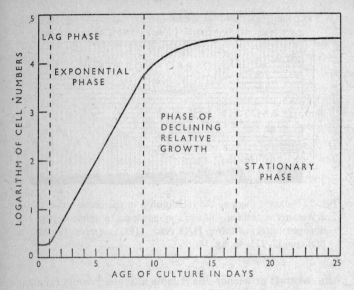

Fig. 2. The growth of *Chlorella* in culture; the logarithm of cell numbers per unit volume of medium is plotted against time.

possible for photosynthesis to continue at a relatively high rate in algae in which cell division has entirely ceased. The materials which were used in the production of fresh protoplasm are then directed along other channels and appear as food reserves and cell wall materials. As a result, the chemical composition of the cells changes and the organic matter of certain strains of *Chlorella* which have been exposed to a bright light for a lengthy period after cell division has ceased may consist of as little as 9 per cent of protein with 6 per cent of carbohydrate and 85 per cent of fat. As well as these changes brought about by alteration in conditions caused by the growth of the alga itself there are variations in chemical composition dependent upon the particular conditions of culture imposed from without. Thus high light intensity in the exponential phase favours a high protein con-

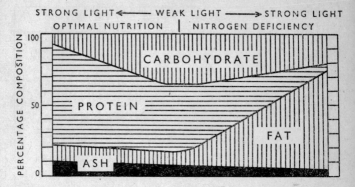

Fig. 3. Diagram showing the relationship of the composition of the dry matter in cells of *Chlorella pyrenoidosa* to light intensity and nitrogen nutrition (after H. G. Aach (1952), *Archiv für Mikrobiologie,* **17,** 213–46, fig. 14).

tent, whereas deficiency of available nitrogen favours fat accumulation. These effects are summarized in Fig. 3.

The explanation of this flexibility in composition is to be found in the nature of the chemical machinery of a living organism. The enzyme-catalyzed reactions which make up this machinery are nearly always reversible and different reactions are so inter-related that enzymes and the substances upon which they act together constitute an integrated system of great plasticity. Material may be introduced into this system at several points, e.g. in *Chlorella* it may be supplied as carbon dioxide and water when the organism is functioning photosynthetically, or as glucose or an organic acid, and the path which it follows through the system is not fixed but varies according to circumstances. When the paths leading to the synthesis of protoplasmic constituents are blocked the material put in appears as reserve products. The difficulty is perhaps not so much to account for the plasticity in chemical composition of *Chlorella* as to explain why it is not even greater than it is and why other organisms should not possess the property in equal measure. The answer to this lies, partly at least, in the fact that in order to live and reproduce an organism must develop certain structures, and this necessitates the production of particular chemical substances, which in turn depends upon particular environmental conditions. *Chlorella* is of relatively simple structure and is tolerant of extreme variations in environmental conditions, and hence this limitation upon variation in chemical composition is at a minimum. Other equally simple and unexacting organisms may show an equal degree of flexibility, although in bacteria and the simpler fungi this is not as evident in the cellular composition as it is in *Chlorella,* because these organisms are able to excrete surplus chemical substances into the surrounding medium to a much greater extent than can *Chlorella.* With more elaborate organisms the internal chemical conditions compatible with development and reproduction become more circumscribed and the limits within which variation in composition is possible become narrower. The chemical composition of an organism such as *Chlorella* is dictated by the environment to a much greater extent than is that of higher plants. More complex plants and animals have developed mechanisms for maintaining a constant internal environment so that their chemical composition is buffered against wide variations produced by changes in the external environment.

With so much fundamental knowledge concerning it available, it becomes important to know how far *Chlorella* is representative of other organisms. Warburg and subsequent workers have assumed that photosynthesis as it occurs in this simple green organism is essentially the same as that which takes place in higher plants with their much greater elaboration of structure and developmental cycle. There seems to be good confirmation of this assumption. The photosynthetic pigments, and in particular chlorophyll a, which appears to be the key substance in this process, are identical in the alga and in higher plants. The primary products of photosynthesis have also been found to be the same in the two types of organism. It is not so certain that other chemical mechanisms in *Chlorella* are similar to those in other types of organisms. The respiration of *Chlorella,* for example, is stimulated by concentrations of cyanide which totally inhibit that of most other forms of life, and this probably indicates a difference of some importance. The general features of growth, nutrition, and metabolism in *Chlorella* are to be seen in other algae, but there is certainly much variation in detail between this and other species. Results obtained with *Chlorella* are sometimes taken as applying to other algae which are less easily investigated experimentally, e.g. those planktonic in lakes and in the oceans. While it is difficult to get an accurate estimate of their abundance, it seems possible that in total bulk of organic matter organisms of this type exceed land plants and, since they are the primary producers in the sea, a knowledge of their activities and behaviour is of practical importance to the fishing industry. However, it is not justifiable to assume that the physiology and biochemistry of these other algae, which are principally diatoms and dinoflagellates, are always similar to those of *Chlorella*. There are included in the algae several classes of organisms which differ profoundly from one another in cell organization and the little knowledge which we have indicates clearly that they also have different biochemical characteristics. Except in a general way, results obtained with representatives of one group cannot be applied to those of another group. A great deal more information about the physiology and biochemistry of algae other than *Chlorella* is, in fact, needed. From our present knowledge it would appear that *Chlorella* is rather exceptional among the simpler algae in its high rate of growth and its tolerance of a wide range of environmental conditions.

Having enjoyed modest fame among plant physiologists and biochemists, *Chlorella* is now beginning to achieve fame, or perhaps notoriety, with a larger public, as a result of the suggestion that it might serve as a source of human food. As it has become realized that human populations are expanding at a greater rate than is agricultural production, search is being made for more efficient ways of growing food materials. The efficiency with which ordinary crop plants use light energy in the photosynthesis of organic materials is rather low – generally less than 1 per cent of the energy of sunlight is converted to chemical energy in this way – and much greater yields per unit area of the earth's surface could evidently be obtained if this efficiency could be increased. However, although the maximum efficiency with which plants can convert the energy of light into chemical energy is of the order of 30 per cent, such rates cannot be approached, except momentarily, with the conventional type of crop plant growing in the field. The reasons for this are several and cannot be fully enumerated here. One important factor is that in its early stages of growth a crop plant intercepts only a small part of the light which falls on the area in which it is planted, and later on as the crop matures the photosynthetic efficiency is decreased as leaves age and are not replaced by fresh ones, so that maximum efficiency is only attained for a small fraction of the growing season and for a still smaller fraction of the whole year. Furthermore, the amount of carbon dioxide in the air is not sufficient to maintain maximum rates of photosynthesis in bright sunlight and increase in its amount generally cannot be achieved economically or without damage to the plant. Apart from the question of efficiency there is also the point that a large proportion of a higher plant is useless as either animal or human food. High photosynthetic efficiencies can be easily achieved and maintained in laboratory cultures of algae such as *Chlorella* and, as we have seen, such forms have the additional advantage that their metabolism may be influenced towards the production of a high proportion of a desired product to a much greater extent than can that of a higher plant. The possibility of using *Chlorella* for industrial photosynthesis has therefore attracted some attention.

The question which is still unsettled is whether it is economically feasible to exploit these properties of *Chlorella* and to grow it in large-scale cultures for the production of material which could be used as food either directly by man himself or for animals which themselves can be used as a source of food. Research on the mass culture of *Chlorella* and other microscopic algae with an eye to its industrial possibilities was begun in Germany during the Second World War and later, but independently, in America. The American work has shown that continuous mass cultures achieving high photosynthetic efficiencies are perfectly possible and that the material produced contains a large proportion of high-grade protein and provides a satisfactory food for rats. However, the initial capital outlay involved in setting up the plant for culture on an industrial scale appears to be prohibitive. It seems at the moment unlikely that *Chlorella* will ever replace the conventional type of crop plant as a producer of human food, for which perhaps there are several reasons for feeling thankful, but it is nevertheless possible that *Chlorella* or some similar organism may be useful in industrial photosynthesis in certain circumstances if its large-scale culture can be simplified or if it is found to contain some particularly valuable constituent to offset the high cost of the culture plant. It might, for example, be useful in arid or soil-less regions or for recovering the valuable plant nutrients in sewage which are at present largely run to waste in the sea. Much as we know about *Chlorella* more remains to be learnt, and it would be strange if nothing of practical value were to emerge from the knowledge of fundamentally important processes which is to be gained by study of this simple plant.

FURTHER READING

Fogg, G. E. (1953), *The Metabolism of Algae*. London, Methuen and Co.

Pearsall, W. H., and Fogg, G. E. (1951), 'The utilization of algae for industrial photosynthesis'. *Food Science Abstracts*, **23**, 1–11.

THE ORIGIN
OF BIOLOGICAL PATTERN

C. H. WADDINGTON

Photogravure illustrations between pp. 64 and 65

IT has always been clear that one of the most advantageous fields for studies in fundamental biology is to be found in the investigation of that stage in which an organism is reduced to its simplest terms; namely, the fertilized egg. During the first thirty years or so of this century, this period of existence has been explored chiefly by tracing out the hereditary transmission of characters under various systems of breeding. A considerable degree of finality has been attained in such studies, although there are, of course, many points still not fully understood; but they seem likely to prove mere matters of specialized detail, though one can never be sure. In the last two decades, however, the centre of the stage has gradually been taken by the problems of development, that is to say of the processes by which the simple elements in the fertilized egg, which represent potentialities, become transformed into the realities of the fully differentiated animal. Thus genetics has turned its main attention to the mechanisms by which genes control the production of particular substances, such as pigments or enzymes. Its centre of interest has shifted until it can scarcely be distinguished from those branches of biology which deal with such problems as the synthesis of proteins, the multiplication of viruses and the developmental functions of cytoplasmic particles.

The recent work on the fundamental processes of development has, in the main, been focused on the problems of the arising of chemical substances, and the physical events involved in the moulding of tissues and organs into definite shapes have received much less attention. This emphasis may have been due, partly, to the feeling – which is probably quite justified – that the chemical processes are the more basic, the physical changes being the consequences of prior chemical conditions rather than *vice versa*; but the direction of scientific effort has undoubtedly also been influenced by a less rational consideration, namely the recent discovery of powerful methods of studying the chemical aspects of gene-action by the use of moulds and other micro-organisms. In a well-balanced biology, however, our understanding of form should be as convincing and illuminating as that of substance. At the present time the field of morphogenesis (the development of shape) offers a perhaps more enticing challenge to the investigator than any other.

Professor J. T. Bonner's recent book, entitled *Morphogenesis; an Essay on Development*,* provides an extraordinarily good review of most of the major problems involved in this complex matter. It is refreshingly free of otiose technicalities; indeed it is one of those scientific treatises, nowadays only too rare, which can be read for pleasure even by those not intimately familiar with its subject. It is greatly to be hoped that it will find the wide audience that it deserves, and that it will open their eyes to the importance and fascination of the topic of which it treats.

Bonner is in his own research a botanist, and he is perhaps slightly more at home among plants than animals. This is, however, a valuable bias, not only because it helps to redress the more usual tendency to over-emphasize the zoological side, but because plant materials offer many striking examples of simple morphogenetic processes. The longest of Bonner's chapters, entitled 'Patterns of Growth,' is devoted to a discussion of many beautifully clear-cut cases of formal arrangements which are produced by control of the orientation of the planes of cell division. If one starts from a single cell, cleavage which occurs always parallel to one plane will convert this into a long filament. An occasional cleavage in a direction which makes some angle with the main one will give rise to cells at which branching occurs; cleavages that are alternately in two planes perpendicular to one another will produce flat sheets of regularly aligned cells, and a similar arrangement with three planes gives cubical

*Princeton University Press; Oxford University Press. 1952. 32s 6d.

colonies. There are no animal examples of such simplicity, but similar processes must be at work not only in forms such as colonial Ciliates, in which individual single-celled organisms hang together to form branched colonies, but also in some particular organs of higher multicellular forms. For example, the shape of the wings of the fruit-fly *Drosophila,* and presumably of other insects, depends in part on the orientations of the cleavage spindles at the time when the cells are multiplying; and genes are known which influence the relative frequencies of orientation along or across the length of the wing.

There are other aspects of biological form which can profitably be discussed in terms of the interactions between cells. It has been emphasized by many authors in recent years that the membranes of different types of cells differ in their 'stickiness' and tendency to adhere to cells of similar or other types. Weiss has suggested that interactions of this sort play a major role in the development of different kinds of cell, by immobilizing certain substances at the surfaces which are in contact, and thus modifying the composition of the internal parts of the cell. This remains largely speculation, and not, perhaps, a very convincing one, since differentiation may occur in completely isolated cells from multicellular organisms as well as in Protozoa, and in neither of these can cell contact-faces play any part.

It is, however, probable that many of the simpler patterns of cellular aggregations depend on the existence of selective affinities, combined with tendencies to expansion or contraction of the membrane according to whether it is in contact with another cell or with a non-cellular medium. Bonner describes some beautiful algal patterns which can probably be explained in this way, and Mookerjee in my laboratory has recently described evidence which suggests that the early morphogenesis of the notochord in the Amphibia is dependent on the same type of phenomenon.

One of the most remarkable examples of morphogenesis which is brought about by the reactions of cells is the formation of the fruit-body in the lowly group of amoeboid slime moulds (Acrasiales), on which Bonner has himself done much of the recent work. In the life-history of these organisms there is a feeding stage, during which the cells are quite separate and wander about in an amoeboid manner, engulfing bacteria and similar particles. If they become thick enough on the ground, a new type of behaviour is initiated; the individual amoebae begin moving towards the region where they are concentrated, and then to adhere loosely together to form a multicellular mass which itself creeps along as a whole, leaving a trail of slimy mucous-like material behind it. After some time, the mass ceases its movement, and rears up into a conical shape, the base of which soon elongates into a relatively thin stalk on top of which is borne a solid, more or less spherical, lump of cells which become spores. Bonner has been able to show that the streaming together of the amoebae is a response to the presence of a substance, which he has called 'acrasin'; the individual cells move along the gradients until they reach the point of highest concentration. Acrasin continues to be produced in the solid mass of adhering cells, but it is not yet clear how far the later phases of morphogenesis which go on in this can also be accounted for as reactions to varying concentrations of the substance. I do not know of any cases quite like this in animals, but it seems not at all improbable that they exist.

Although, as has been shown by the examples which have been mentioned, many morphogenetic events find their explanation in terms of the relations between cells, there is no doubt that there are many others for which explanations of that kind are inappropriate. In particular, the most important of all aspects of morphogenesis, the initial arising of a pattern in a mass which previously appeared quite homogeneous, can hardly be dealt with by theories which are content to take cells as their ultimate units. There are too many examples in which patterns arise either within single cells (and thus demand a theory dealing in sub-cellular units) or within large multicellular masses (where they seem to call for super-cellular considerations).

In some cases of intra-cellular patterns it is very tempting to suppose that the phenomena which we can see are expressions of the structure of the underlying molecules. For instance, in some genera of snails, of which the common *Limnea* of our ponds is the best example in this country, there are two forms of shell, one with a right-handed and one with a left-handed spiral. Breeding experiments have shown that the difference between the two forms depends on a simple Mendelian gene, but one which has the peculiar feature that it acts in the animal's ovary and determines the kind of eggs which it will produce, so that all the offspring of a given snail will coil in the same direction; the genes they received from their father's sperm have no immediate influence, but affect only the kind of eggs which will be produced to make the next generation. The question is, how does the gene act to determine the symmetry of the coiling? One possibility would be that it controlled the production of either right- or left-handed spirally shaped protein molecules – there are grounds for thinking that proteins may sometimes have spiral molecules. But if this were so, it would seem probable that the sperm of *Limnea*, which also have a spiral structure, would show the effects of the same gene. Dr Selman and I have recently looked at the sperm in the electron microscope, but we found that, whatever the genetic constitution of the animal with respect to the coiling of its shell and eggs, the sperm were always spiralized in the same direction. So the basis for the egg pattern has to be looked for elsewhere. (Plate 8.)

It is still very difficult to know in what direction one is most likely to find it. As Bonner says, 'There is a general theory to cover every aspect of the control of growth save one, and that is the problem of *the configuration within the whole organism*.' There have been several recent attempts to tackle the problem theoretically. Perhaps the most radical is that of Turing. In a paper with the challenging title of 'The Chemical Basis of Morphogenesis',* he has suggested a mechanism by which a regular pattern might arise within a completely homogeneous system. He considers a region (imagine a plane two-dimensional area to make it simpler) in which a number of chemical reactions are proceeding. If these interact with one another by involving the same substances, or by producing products which act as

Phil. Trans. Roy. Soc. B, vol. 237, pp. 37–72.

catalysts or affect the rates of other reactions in any way, then the straightforward situation would be the attainment of some sort of balanced equilibrium condition throughout the whole area. But such an equilibrium is only a statistical phenomenon; actually the system will be disturbed by slight chance variations from place to place. Now it is easy to imagine special systems of reactions such that the equilibrium is unstable; if by chance one substance appears at a certain place in slightly too high a concentration, it will go on increasing. From each such 'high' spot, the substance will diffuse outwards, so that the spots will gradually enlarge. Turing has set up mathematical equations for such systems and, choosing some arbitrary figures to express the rates of the reactions and of the diffusions, has solved them by means of a modern computing machine. He found that under certain conditions one might expect to get a pattern of a few fairly large spots or irregular blotches of high values of some particular substance. Moreover, in some circumstances the pattern might be more regular, showing a rhythm with a definite wave-length dependent on the physical and chemical magnitudes controlling the reactions.

Turing compares his 'chemical wave-length' with the interval between regularly appearing structures in an animal or plant. For instance, if the circumference of the cylindrical body of a Hydra were just about six times the wave-length, one might attribute the animal's radial symmetry, and the appearance of six tentacles, to such a mechanism. But here, it seems to me, Turing is going too far. One of the major characteristics of animal patterns is that they tend to appear as complete units without much reference to the quantity of material available; a normally shaped newt can develop from a half egg, or from two eggs fused together, just as well as from a normal single egg. The intervals between the various elements in the pattern are almost certainly not determined by invariant chemical rate constants of the kind Turing envisages.

The demonstration that patterns may arise as a consequence of chance variations around an equilibrium is, however, an important one. It probably finds its best exemplification in such

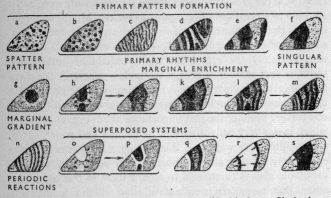

PRIMARY PATTERN FORMATION

SPATTER PATTERN   PRIMARY RHYTHMS MARGINAL ENRICHMENT   SINGULAR PATTERN

MARGINAL GRADIENT   SUPERPOSED SYSTEMS

PERIODIC REACTIONS

Basic types of pattern formation, as exemplified in butterflies' wings. (After Henke, *Naturwissenschaften*, 1948, Vol. **35**, p. 176.)

phenomena as the colour patterns on butterflies' wings, animals' coats and such things. Henke, who has made a considerable study of such patterns, has attempted to classify them in accordance with the various types of originating mechanisms to which they are due. (Fig. 1). His most elementary stage, like that of Turing, is the appearance of abnormal spots of varying size scattered by chance throughout the area (*a*); and he also suggests (though without the same imposing mathematical apparatus to back him up) that rhythmic patterns will be developed from them (*b* to *e*). As an extreme case, the area may only be large enough for a single element of the rhythm; so we get a 'singular pattern' (*f*). Henke then goes on to consider the ways in which such a basic pattern may grow in complexity; for instance, a zone of gradation may appear round the margin of a spot (*g*); or there may be an accumulation of substances at the boundary between two different areas (*h, i*); a second chemically differentiated area may appear later inside an earlier-formed one (*o, p, q*); or periodic precipitations of the Liesegang type may occur (*n*); and by combinations of these processes still more complex patterns may be built up (*k, l, m, r, s*).

It is only rather rarely that the student of higher organisms is faced with the problem of accounting for the arising of a pattern *de novo* in a previously homogeneous system. Much more commonly, the phenomenon which confronts us is the gradual elaboration of an originally simple system into a more complex one. Certainly the egg, from which individual development starts, is very seldom, if ever, a featureless sphere; it has a certain inherent structure which it owes largely to the geometry of the processes by which it is formed in the ovary. But there is one further point of the first importance about organic patterns, which is not very fully discussed by Bonner and which certain eggs exhibit very well. It is this; biological patterns are often expressions of dynamic equilibrium, and perhaps it would be profitable always to attempt to regard them in this light. That means that the pattern is not a static affair which is formed once for all and is merely there; on the contrary, it can be shown for many patterns that they are actively maintaining themselves all the time, and if they are disturbed the various elements tend to shift around again until they have restored their original arrangement in relation to each other. For instance, the most important part of the initial pattern of the egg of many snails and worms is the formation of special regions of cytoplasm just under the surface at the two opposite poles (animal and vegetative) of the egg. If these polar plasms are shifted, by centrifuging, away from their original location, they soon succeed in moving back. There would appear to be some specific attraction between the polar plasms and the corresponding polar regions of the cell membrane. We have almost no idea of the nature of such attractions, but their existence shows that, in order to account for biological pattern, we may have to take account of more subtle concepts than the simple ones of diffusion, reaction-rates and so on with which theory is trying to get along now.

FOR FURTHER READING

Essays on Growth and Form (1945), edited by W. E. Le Gros Clark and P. B. Medawar. Oxford University Press.

Child, C. M. (1941). *Patterns and Problems of Development*. Chicago University Press.

Needham, J. (1936). *Order and Life*. Yale University Press.

Waddington, C. H. (1940). *Organisers and Genes*. Cambridge University Press.

SOME RECENT BIOLOGICAL BOOKS

A SELECT list of recent publications which the editors consider should be brought to the notice of readers of *New Biology*.

The Changing Wild Life of Britain by H. L. Edlin (London, Batsford, 1952), 184 pp., 113 half-tone figures, 21s. Our fauna and flora have been as much enriched as impoverished by human activities. How many people know the number of species of deer now running wild in England? This book contains much interesting information which stresses the dynamics of our natural history.

Animals and Man by G. S. Cansdale (London, Hutchinson, 1952), 200 pp., 31 half-tone plates, 15s. Like Edlin's book, deals with the impact of man on the populations of some species of animal, though on a world scale. Likewise an attractively presented picture of the dynamics of natural history.

The Watcher and the Red Deer by Richard Perry (Edinburgh, William Hodge, 1952), 188 pp., 15s. Intense and devoted observation round the year by a distinguished naturalist of a superb and threatened member of our fauna.

Journey into Wonder by N. J. Berrill (London, Victor Gollancz, 1953), 320 pp., 13s 6d. An account from the biologist's point of view of some of the great voyages which opened up the world. Fascinating in its enthusiasm and erudition.

Poplars by T. R. Peace, 50 pp., 24 half-tone plates, 1952, 17s 6d. *Studies on British Beechwoods* by J. M. B. Brown, 100 pp., 28 half-tones plates, 1953, 12s 6d. Forestry Commission Bullettins, Nos. 19 and 20. (London, H.M. Stationery Office.) Detailed accounts of ecology and silviculture of two attractive kinds of tree, with many fine photographs.

A Physiological Approach to the Lower Animals by J. A. Ramsay (Cambridge, The University Press, 1952), 148 pp., 15s. Considers how invertebrates solve some of the main problems posed by their environments. An excellent introduction to the variety of the animal kingdom on the functional side, requiring a little zoological and chemical background.

Abraham Trembley of Geneva: Scientist and Philosopher: 1710–1784 by John R. Baker (London, Edward Arnold, 1952), 259 pp., 52 illustrations, 35s. Trembley was one of the greatest experimental zoologists, the first to prove asexual reproduction by budding, the first to multiply animals artificially, the first to graft animals successfully. But above all he was and is a model scientist, extraordinary in that, through his exquisite awareness of the relation between hypothesis and observation, he almost never went wrong. Baker draws a fascinating picture of a great mind and its times, going back to original sources for all his information.

What is Race? Evidence from Scientists (London, H.M. Stationery Office for UNESCO), 87 pp., 5s. A simple illustrated booklet intended for mass eradication of racial fallacies, based on expert advice. Interesting example of applied popular biology.

Biology and Language. An introduction to the Methodology of the Biological Sciences including Medicine by J. H. Woodger (Cambridge, The University Press, 1952), 364 pp., 40s. A critical examination of the language in which biological knowledge, especially genetical and neurological theory, is stored and communicated. Very important for those interested in the philosophy of biology. Contains a good deal expressed in symbolic form.

ABOUT OUR CONTRIBUTORS

J. B. S. HALDANE, F.R.S., was formerly Reader in Biochemistry at Cambridge, and since 1933 has been Professor of Biometry at University College, London.

REGINALD CHILD. Graduated in Chemistry in 1923 at King's College, London, where subsequently he did research on organic sulphur compounds. From 1927 to 1930 was in the Research Department of Boots Pure Drug Co. Ltd, working on synthetic alkaloids. 1931–49, Director, Coconut Research Institute, Ceylon. 1950 to date, Senior Chemist, Tea Research Institute of East Africa (Kericho, Kenya Colony).

RICHARD PERRY, B.A., has been a field naturalist every day for 20 years; has made expeditions each of half a year to Lundy and to Noss (Shetland) to watch sea birds; and has made observations of birds in many other parts of the British Isles. Author of *The Watcher and the Red Deer* (1952), *Shetland Sanctuary* (1948), *A Naturalist on Lindisfarne* (1946), *Lundy : Isle of Puffins* (1940), and many other works. He wrote an article on gannets for *New Biology 10*.

M. L. JOHNSON, PH.D., is a zoologist now working on problems of training medical students in the Anatomy Department of University College, London, supported by the Rockefeller Foundation. She has contributed articles on Malaria and the Tapeworm to *New Biology 1* and *7*.

JOHN E. HARRIS, PH.D., is Professor of Zoology at the University of Bristol. He has worked on many aspects of zoology: on the physical structure of protoplasm (see his article in *New Biology 5*), on fish locomotion, on the biology of ship fouling, on radio-active tracers (see his article in *New Biology 10*), and is now investigating the development of behaviour patterns in the dogfish embryo.

G. E. FOGG, B.SC., PH.D., Reader in Botany at University College, London, has contributed articles on 'Blue-Green Algae', 'The Wetting of Leaves by Water', and 'The Mechanism of Photosynthesis' to *New Biology 5, 10*, and *11*.

C. H. WADDINGTON, F.R.S., is one of the best known of present-day embryologists and geneticists. He is Professor of Genetics and head of the Institute of Animal Genetics in the University of Edinburgh.